This book is a gift to:

_____

From:

_____

Date:

_____

"Your Mother Has Alzheimer's"

Three daughters answer their father's call.

Margaret Byers • Ann Guyer • Nancy Willich

Cord Publications, LLC • Ponte Vedra Beach, Florida

"Your Mother Has Alzheimer's"
Three daughters answer their father's call.

Acord Publications, LLC
P.O. Box 979
Ponte Vedra Beach, FL 32004
877-577-8885
acordof@aol.com
www.yourmotherhasalzheimers.com

Scripture Quotations:

Scripture taken from the NEW AMERICAN STANDARD BIBLE ®, Copyright © 1960, 1962, 1963, 1968, 1971, 1972, 1973, 1975, 1977, 1995 by The Lockman Foundation. Used by permission.

Scripture taken from the HOLY BIBLE, NEW INTERNATIONAL VERSION ®. Copyright © 1973, 1978, 1984 by International Bible Society. Used by permission of Zondervan. All rights reserved.

Scripture taken from the New King James Version. Copyright © 1979, 1980, 1982 by Thomas Nelson, Inc. Used by permission. All rights reserved.

Scripture quotations are taken from the Holy Bible, New Living Translation, Copyright © 1996. Used by permission of Tyndale House Publishers, Inc., Wheaton, IL 60189. All rights reserved.

KJV - King James Version   NASB - New American Standard Bible
NIV - New International Version   NKJV - New King James Version
NLT - New Living Translation

All references to God are capitalized.

Cover Illustration and Chapter Icons by Jacqueline Bray

Printed by Worzalla Publishing, Stevens Point, Wisconsin 54481

Printed in the United States of America

ISBN: 0-9773352-0-8

To our father and mother,
Alfred Louis Nimz and Ruth Moen Nason Nimz,
A caregiver and his loved one

PON

HWY 44

SPALDING

HALL

JACKSON

SCOTT

TYGERT

GOTHIC MILL
POND

Heavenly Father, You are the light that penetrates our darkest moments. Thank You for showing us so clearly that You are our Guide on every step of this journey. We pray that this book will provide answers and encouragement to everyone who seeks help in its pages.

We ask that each reader will be continually aware of Your presence and be blessed by the opportunity to grow closer to family and closer to You. Help all of us not only to accept Your plan for our lives but to embrace it. Thy will be done. In Jesus' name, Amen.

Table of Contents

Introduction

This book is for anyone who is involved in the life of an Alzheimer's sufferer, whether you are serving on the front lines daily or lending a helping hand occasionally. We specifically address the roles of the primary caregiver and those assisting with day-to-day support. We have asked ourselves over and over again as we wrote each chapter, "What information would have been helpful to us when we were at this stage in the progression of the disease?" You will find our answers to that question in the pages of this book.

"Your Mother Has Alzheimer's" includes selected episodes from our family's story to illustrate the lessons we've learned. The issues raised by these narratives are then addressed through practical advice and specific guidance based on our unique experience. You will also find prayers for those times when you want to talk with God and words fail you. Each chapter closes with references from God's Word to help you come to see Alzheimer's as we have—not as a tragedy but, amazingly, as a blessing, part of God's plan for bringing us closer to Him and to each other.

In writing *"Your Mother Has Alzheimer's"* and reflecting on the impact of the disease on our family, we realized that we had done quite well in meeting a number of challenges and not so well in meeting others. Most important was the realization that God's hand was in the whole process, even when we weren't aware of it. When we did seek Him, we often saw His plan unfolding. Through this experience, we three sisters have grown closer to one another and to our Creator. We pray that you and your family will have the same blessing.

Encountering God's Word

JOHN 1:4–5 NLT

Life itself was in Him, and this life gives light to everyone. The light shines through the darkness, and the darkness can never extinguish it.

Chapter 1: Early Signs of Alzheimer's

What's happening?

Peggy's Story

"Hi, Nance. Are you ready to go? I'm really glad we decided to drive Mom and Dad to the wedding. Ann will be a beautiful mother of the bride. I can't wait to get there."

Nancy and I left Virginia in high spirits. We loved traveling together with Sammy, Nancy's golden retriever, as our eager companion. Taking our parents to their granddaughter's wedding was a journey we had anticipated for several months. We had no idea that the journey we were starting was not just for the weekend but would span more than a decade and take us to a place far from a quiet colonial church in Minneapolis.

As sunlight flooded the sanctuary, the beauty of the ceremony took us back to our own weddings. We were touched to see our parents holding hands as the bride and groom exchanged their vows. The service came to an end, and the crowd started filing out.

"Come on, Mom. Here's a little jar of bubbles. They're using them instead of rice. Let's hurry. We don't want to miss the fun." Everyone from the youngest to the oldest joined in sending the newlyweds off from the church in a shower of bubbles.

We were so caught up in the moment that we didn't notice Mom wandering off from the happy gathering. I saw just a glimpse of periwinkle blue as she disappeared around the corner of the church, heading for the darkness of the woods beyond. I was concerned. I couldn't figure out where she was going. As I started after her, I called to Nancy and Dad, "Do you know where Mom's going?"

Nancy looked puzzled, but Dad looked alarmed and called out, "Peg, hurry up. Don't lose sight of her." My pace quickened.

I rounded the corner and was struck by the picture of Mom walking away from us and into a totally unfamiliar area. "Mom, where are you going? Mom. Mother. Can you hear me?" When she didn't respond to my increasingly anxious calls, I ran after her. As I reached out to her and put my hand in hers, she turned to face me. I saw a look in her eyes I had never seen before but would come to know all too well. I was looking into the bewildered eyes of Alzheimer's disease.

> 1 PETER 5:7 NLT
>
> *Give all your worries and cares to God, for He cares about what happens to you.*

Ann's Story

"Mom and Pops, let's sit over by the window. There's a great view of the city from up here. The lights are beautiful, and you can see the whole downtown so clearly."

I was glad I finally had a chance to sit down, slip my shoes off, and visit with my parents. Their presence at my daughter's wedding meant so much to me. They had seemed like newlyweds themselves earlier at the reception. When the guests tapped their glasses to urge the bride and groom to embrace, Mom and Dad stood up. They stole the show with a kiss of their own. I hoped my daughter's marriage would be as rock solid as theirs in 54 years.

As the younger guests took to the dance floor, I was delighted to spend a few quiet moments with my folks. Dad began pointing out landmarks in the skyline.

"I think that's the IDS building over there, and that's the Metro Dome."

"Mom, did you hear what Dad said? There's the Metro Dome. That's where the Packers will beat the Vikings next month."

She was a huge Green Bay Packers fan. I thought she'd be eager to see where they'd be playing, but she seemed disinterested, almost distracted. "Mom, what are you looking at?"

"I'm looking at that train in the sky." She pointed to a large, brightly lit billboard.

"Mom, that's a billboard. Can't you see the writing and the picture of the guy catching the fish?" Despite our efforts, Dad and I could not convince her that the billboard was reality, that there was no train in the sky. I just didn't understand why she couldn't see what was really there.

> 2 CORINTHIANS 4:18 NIV
>
> *So we fix our eyes not on what is seen, but on what is unseen. For what is seen is temporary, but what is unseen is eternal.*

Mom was ready to leave the reception a short time later. Before Dad took her back to their room, I gave her a hug—not a quick good-night hug but a long and loving hug, a prayer-filled hug.

Nancy's Story

"Good morning. It's your dancing daughters. Father, didn't we have fun keeping the band busy last night? And now, here you are ready to go again. Well, this is a switch. Mom, you're always waiting for Dad. Peg, why don't Dad and I go ahead to the brunch and save you seats? Mom, Peggy'll wait and come with you."

I was surprised that Mom wasn't ready on time for the post-wedding brunch, especially since she'd left the reception so early the night before. It was not like her to be running behind schedule.

"Father, what's with Mom not being ready?"

"She'll be down in a minute. She's been having a little trouble getting organized lately. Sometimes it takes her a little longer to get dressed."

"Is everything okay?"

"Oh, we're doing fine."

We had arrived at the brunch, so I let the subject drop, but I made a mental note to bring it up with my sisters later. Mom and Peggy arrived half an hour late, but the guests were just starting to eat. I was pleased to see how many people came over to greet the grandparents of the bride. Several of them even commented on Mom and Dad's impromptu kiss of the night before.

As people stopped by our table, Dad greeted each one by name, but it quickly became obvious that Mom couldn't recall any names, and her greeting to each person was "Isn't it a beautiful day?" Mom had a degree in journalism and was a skilled conversationalist. How could she be at a loss for words?

Later, as we left the Minneapolis city limits behind us, I couldn't help but wonder what else we were leaving behind. Was the mother we had known all our lives gone forever? Had she gone around

> PHILIPPIANS 4:6–7 NIV
>
> *Do not be anxious about anything, but in everything, by prayer and petition, with thanksgiving, present your requests to God. And the peace of God, which transcends all understanding, will guard your hearts and your minds in Christ Jesus.*

the corner at the church in her periwinkle blue dress never to return? Peggy and I stole quick glances at the woman sitting next to our father and wondered, "What's happening to our mother?"

Your Guide

"Girls, your mother has Alzheimer's." Dad's news had been devastating. When each of us had last seen Mom and Dad, everything seemed fine. They were enjoying their home in a lovely little college town in Wisconsin and had been doing some traveling; their lives seemed perfectly normal.

We three daughters were all busy with careers, businesses, and families—caught up in the time of life between becoming empty nesters and heading into retirement. Although we always enjoyed getting together, at the time we found out about our mother's Alzheimer's, we lived very separate lives. We begin our story from that perspective. We were attending a family event together, but we believed that when it was over, we would return to our individual lives. For this reason, the first chapter begins with each of us observing the symptoms of the disease separately. In the weeks following the wedding, we realized that our mother's illness and our father's role as primary caregiver needed our collective efforts. God blessed us with the gift of unity, and that is how the remaining chapters of this book are written—with one voice.

> ECCLESIASTES 4:12b NIV
> *A cord of three strands is not quickly broken.*

We have included in each chapter:

- *A story*—the heart of our experience

- *A guide*—specific advice to help you

- *A prayer*—coming to God in each phase of Alzheimer's

- *Scriptures*—the power of God's Word

Do you have concerns about someone close to you who may be exhibiting early signs of Alzheimer's disease? This chapter addresses symptoms that may be caused by Alzheimer's, dementia, stress, stroke, or a variety of other medical conditions. We focus on symptoms that we observed in our mother and other Alzheimer's sufferers whom we have come to know as her illness progressed. We aren't offering medical advice, but we urge you to seek it. Recent developments in combating the disease include diagnostic tests and medications designed to slow the progression of symptoms. To take advantage of these and other advances, we encourage you to seek medical assistance as soon as possible and keep informed of what's happening in the field.

As we write this book, we have had three family members diagnosed with Alzheimer's. Although they have exhibited some of the same behaviors, we have also learned that no two sets of Alzheimer's symptoms are alike. In some people, the disease advances more slowly than in others, and not all indications are present in all sufferers. Some symptoms appear and never go away; others come and go. The advance of Alzheimer's isn't steady or predictable.

What is predictable about Alzheimer's is the early loss of verbal skills. Some sufferers respond to this symptom by withdrawing and becoming quieter. Others remain very verbal, using the wrong word without realizing it or becoming frustrated with their inability to come up with the right word. Many adapt to these new challenges by depending on stock phrases that are acceptable in any situation.

One of the first verbal symptoms we noticed in Mom was her inability to come up with the right word to complete a sentence. She would substitute something completely unrelated, never realizing her mistake. For instance, when Mom needed help with the buttons on the back of her dress, she said to one of us, "I'm having trouble with these blossoms." What makes this substitution unique to Alzheimer's is her inability to recognize her mistake. Although we all misspeak from time to time, we usually catch ourselves or recognize the error when others point it out to us. Mom had no idea that she had said the wrong word. When we chuckled and said, "Those aren't blossoms, Mom. They're buttons," she looked bewildered.

In conversation, Mom came to rely on generic phrases, such as "It's a busy time of year" or "Isn't it a nice day?" because these were safe and could be used in virtually any situation.

> MATTHEW 24:35 NLT
>
> *"Heaven and earth will disappear, but My words will remain forever."*

We also noticed that she asked more questions, encouraging others to assume more responsibility for conversations: "How's the family?" or "What have you been doing lately?" These were attempts to hide her loss of verbal skills, and to some extent, they were effective. Many neighbors and casual acquaintances were unaware of the progression of her disease.

Short-term memory loss, a related early symptom, quickly robs Alzheimer's sufferers of their ability to follow daily routines. Sleep patterns change; sufferers are often up and about during the night, not realizing when they are tired. Some may not remember to shower and may wear the same clothes day after day. They may start losing weight because they forget to eat or even forget that they are in the middle of eating. Mom's meal would be interrupted by a phone call, and she would forget to return to the table.

We were sad when Mom could no longer enjoy two of her favorite forms of relaxation—reading and watching the Wisconsin Badgers or Green Bay Packers on TV. She had lost the ability to follow the plots of even simple novels, and the complexity of football became too much for her to understand.

Organizational skills also slip away. People with Alzheimer's become unable to:

- Cook and store food properly
- Find their way to familiar locations
- Drive a car safely
- Handle money and shop independently
- Make telephone calls and use the answering machine
- Return household items to their proper places, resulting in constant searches for things that have been lost

Many of those afflicted with Alzheimer's desperately try to restore order to their confusing lives. Mom became obsessed with starting projects that would not have made sense to her before the onset of the disease. She took her recipe cards out of their categories and worked for months trying to alphabetize them—unsuccessfully. She seemed to be trying to organize at least one small portion of her life.

Alzheimer's robs its sufferers of their ability to contribute in ways that they had previously enjoyed. As Mom was forced to give up her volunteer work for the church, the library, the historical society, and her political party, as well as writing projects for various causes, it was important for her to find other pastimes. One activity that filled the void was picking up leaves. She would do it endlessly, seemingly tirelessly.

> RUTH 2:7 NIV
>
> *"She said, 'Please let me glean and gather among the sheaves behind the harvesters.' She went into the field and has worked steadily from morning till now, except for a short rest in the shelter."*

This almost obsessive behavior carried over indoors. Mom and Dad's visit to Ann's first-grade classroom at the end of a busy school day provides a good example. When the principal stopped in, Mom was so preoccupied with picking up every tiny piece of paper off the floor that she barely acknowledged Beth's attempts to welcome her to the school. Even Ann's gentle reminder that the custodians vacuumed every evening did not distract Mom from her compulsive need to accomplish something.

We were amazed at how long our 70-year-old mother could stay bent over at these labors. Upon reflection, we suspected that she no longer sensed pain in the way that she had previously. This suspicion was reinforced later when she acquired a case of shingles, which is usually extremely painful. Over the weeks she was infected, she exhibited absolutely no signs of pain.

The symptoms that are most difficult to understand and cope with are the ones that are emotionally charged for both the person with Alzheimer's and the caregiver. It's common for Alzheimer's sufferers to hide things. Your loved one may accuse you and others of stealing, sometimes the very items he or she has hidden. The fears and frustrations of the person with Alzheimer's can turn to displays of anger that are completely out of character. Extreme jealousy and paranoia are relatively short-term symptoms that can be minimized with proper medication and distraction (see chapter 6).

Dealing with our mother's symptoms was incredibly difficult. At times, we all suffered needlessly because we didn't know what to expect, how to handle Mom's symptoms in the short term, how to support Dad in the best way, when to turn to others for help, and how to cope with our own feelings over time. These were all lessons we would learn during the course of our mother's illness. By trusting in God's guidance, we were able to overcome the challenges we faced.

With the onset of Alzheimer's symptoms in our mother, we were confused and concerned. We found comfort, wisdom, and guidance in the Bible. God also spoke to us in our prayers, through other people, and through circumstances in our lives.

> **PSALM 119:105 KJV**
>
> *Thy Word is a lamp unto my feet,*
> *And a light unto my path.*

Our family was in a dark place, but God, Who is faithful and full of grace, brought light to our darkness.

A Prayer

Heavenly Father, You are the true source of comfort and peace, our refuge and our strength. Thank You for Your loving presence in our lives. We need You, Lord. We are confused and concerned and don't understand what's happening. Help us to be strong and deliver us from our fears. Help us to always turn first to You in times of need and to trust that You will hear our prayers. Thy will be done. In Jesus' name, Amen.

Comfort from God's Word

JOHN 14:27 NIV

"Peace I leave with you; My peace I give you. I do not give to you as the world gives. Do not let your hearts be troubled and do not be afraid."

Additional Scriptures

EXODUS 15:13 NIV

> *"In Your unfailing love You will lead*
> *the people You have redeemed.*
> *In Your strength You will guide them*
> *to Your holy dwelling."*

PSALM 34:4 NIV

> *I sought the LORD, and He answered me;*
> *He delivered me from all my fears.*

PROVERBS 3:5–6 KJV

> *Trust in the LORD with all thine heart;*
> *And lean not unto thine own understanding.*
> *In all thy ways acknowledge Him,*
> *And He shall direct thy paths.*

ISAIAH 46:4 NLT

> *"I will be your God throughout your lifetime—until your hair*
> *is white with age. I made you, and I will care for you. I will*
> *carry you along and save you."*

LUKE 11:9–10 NIV

> *"So I say to you: Ask and it will be given to you; seek and*
> *you will find; knock and the door will be opened to you. For*
> *everyone who asks receives; he who seeks finds; and to him who*
> *knocks, the door will be opened."*

LUKE 12:22, 25 NIV

> *Then Jesus said to his disciples: "… Who of you by worrying*
> *can add a single hour to his life?"*

ROMANS 8:26–27 NIV

In the same way, the Spirit helps us in our weakness. We do not know what we ought to pray for, but the Spirit Himself intercedes for us with groans that words cannot express. And He Who searches our hearts knows the mind of the Spirit, because the Spirit intercedes for the saints in accordance with God's will.

Chapter 2: Facing the Future

What can we still do together?

Our Story

> *"Ann and Nance, are you both on the line?...Good...Have you talked with Mom and Dad lately? They'd like us to come to the cottage for a weekend."*

Camp Onahill, our family cottage, is on the Chain of Lakes near Waupaca, Wisconsin. It was built in 1927 by our great grandparents, and over the years, six generations of the family have gathered there throughout the summer months. As we walked down the rough, uneven steps, we didn't need our eyes to know we were at "the cottage." The combined smells of the pine trees and Sunset Lake told us. We called out the family's traditional announcement of arrival: "Yoo hoo!" Mom and Dad echoed our greeting, and our weekend had begun.

We had a great time. We spent hours on the large screened-in porch, which was the center of family activity.

Laughter rang out as we recalled the many happy times we'd spent there. Mom had camped at the cottage every summer since she was nine years old. She was able to share so much family history and enjoyed reliving the happy summers of her youth. Dad had a lot more to say as we moved on to stories about our family vacations there when the three of us were young.

> PSALM 118:24 NIV
>
> *This is the day the LORD has made;*
> *let us rejoice and be glad in it.*

Late Saturday morning, Mom took us down to the lake to see the forget-me-nots she and Aunt Dorie had planted along the shoreline. It was one of the many projects she and Dorie had worked on together. The two women had planted them in loving memory of family and friends, campers who were among the first to make their summer homes on the north shore. The tiny flowers had spread over the years into beautiful patches of blue splashed across four properties.

We weren't really surprised when we got back up to the cottage and found Dad asleep. He was stretched out on the swing that had been hanging at the end of the porch for as long as we could remember. It was a favorite spot for afternoon naps for the adults and make-believe train rides for generations of young campers.

We knew Dad needed to get some rest, so we left him a note and headed out for lunch and shopping.

Mom was thrilled to be spending an afternoon with her three daughters. "Let's eat at the King's Table," she suggested.

"That works for me. I'm hungry."

"Good idea. While we eat, we can plan which shops we have time to visit. There are so many great ones. I can never decide."

We wound our way through the woods past Otter Lake and headed over to King. As we drove toward the restaurant, Mom pointed to one of the picturesque little shops and said, "I think I've been there."

Peggy gently prompted Mom: "You're right. That's Cate and Company, and it's one of your favorites. Let's make that our first stop after lunch."

We did just that, and loaded down with treasures from Cate's and several other shops, we stopped for ice cream at Country Greetings.

We often saved the Red Mill until last. We relished the opportunity to shop, then linger on the banks of the Crystal River. As we got out of the car, we could hear the familiar sound of the rushing water that had once provided power for the mill.

Browsing our way through both floors of the shop took quite a while. We put our purchases in the car and walked down the narrow steps to the river's edge. We strolled along the sandy path and crossed the covered bridge on our way to the chapel in the woods.

Mom went straight into the chapel. A few minutes later, we headed in to join her but paused just inside the doorway. God's presence was so evident: the sun filtering through the beautiful stained-glass windows; the large cross, its clear glass providing a glimpse of the tall trees outside; and the peace and serenity reflected in the expression on Mom's face as she sat in the comfort of His house.

Ann motioned to Nancy to capture the moment on film. It's a photograph we all treasure.

We had returned from church the next day and were finishing the lunch dishes when we heard a "Yoo hoo." Our cousins Susan and Chuck came down the steps and in the screen door. It was good to see them. Chuck was in the process of buying our parents' share of the cottage. Mom and Dad no longer felt at ease there alone, and the upkeep was too much work for them. Knowing that Chuck would keep Camp Onahill in the family was a comfort. He had given Mom a special gold key so that she and Dad could spend time there whenever they wished.

As children, we five cousins swam, fished, boated, and played games at the lake under the watchful eyes of three generations of adults. Our Great Aunt Lede was a lifelong learner and teacher. She was interested in everything and shared her enthusiasm for innumerable activities with us—picking wild flowers, watching birds, cooking, playing games, going to Whispering Pines Park, listening to Milwaukee Braves baseball on the radio, setting a proper table, wading in Beasley Creek, taking us for a round of miniature golf—the list was endless.

On Friday nights, Aunt Lede would pile the five of us into her car and head for town. We'd meet the rest of the family for band concerts on the town square. While the adults relaxed on park benches, visiting and listening to the music, we kids never sat still. We ran between the cotton-candy man and the pop-corn cart and the ice-cream vendor—always racing to be first in line.

Aunt Lede made shopping trips an adventure. We never went to a supermarket, but the markets we frequented were always super. Aunt Lede introduced us to home-grown vegetables from Mrs. Genetti's garden, farm-fresh eggs from Mrs. Taylor's chickens, berries and asparagus we gathered near Emmons Creek. To this day, nothing tastes sweeter than Turner's freshly picked sweet corn.

Meals at Onahill were a family affair. Everyone had a job—from Great Grandma Moen kneading the dough for her home-made bread to the youngsters shucking corn in the back yard. Each meal began with a prayer. As much as we enjoyed those meals, we were being nourished by more than the earthly food that was spread before us. The foundations of our faith were being laid at that table. We could not know the importance of the gift we were being given those summers—a faith that would sustain us through good times and bad, even through our darkest days with Alzheimer's.

> PSALM 78:4b NIV
>
> *...we will tell the next generation the praiseworthy deeds of the LORD, His power, and the wonders He has done.*

Although the carefree summers of our youth were now far behind us, the lessons learned around that long wooden table had prepared us for the changes and challenges that lay ahead. It was no coincidence that we were drawn to the cottage and to our family at this time. Susan and Chuck had already been through much of what we were facing. Their father was Mom's only sibling and had recently passed away from complications of Alzheimer's disease. Our cousins' experience and support would help us through some of the critical times ahead.

God had blessed us with a beautiful day in which to enjoy His creation, and we did just that. Chuck offered to serve as captain on a pontoon boat ride through the lakes. He slowed his pace to match the rhythm of the day, enabling us to savor the moments.

The paddlewheel boat passed, and we waved to the sightseers on the deck. Chuck was sensitive to the changes his purchase of the cottage would bring for Mom and Dad. "Uncle Al, if you and Aunt Ruth come up when I'm not here to help with the boat, get yourselves some tickets on the paddlewheel at Clearwater Harbor. They have a nice evening dinner cruise."

Chuck obviously knew a lot more about where the disease would be taking them than we did. He was already encouraging them to look beyond what they could no longer do. He knew it was time for them to adapt to their changing world by finding new

> PSALM 103:17 NIV
>
> *But from everlasting to everlasting*
> *the LORD's love is with those who fear Him,*
> *and His righteousness with their children's*
> *children—*

ways to do old things. In the days ahead, they would need help finding new activities to replace the ones they'd lost.

After Susan and Chuck left that evening, we gathered in the living room. Sitting in front of the old stone fireplace, we listened to music of the 30s. We had specifically chosen selections that would be meaningful to Mom. As a teenager, she had danced to many of these tunes on Saturday nights when the big bands came to the dance hall on Columbia Lake.

Dad rose to his feet. We thought he was heading for bed, but he turned and walked over to Mom. "Have you left a place for me on your dance card, Luv?" She reached up and took his hand, and they danced by the light of the fire as if they were all alone in the room.

Your Guide

Dancing was one activity that Mom and Dad continued to enjoy for many years after Mom's diagnosis. As the disease progressed, we were pleased when we saw our parents involve themselves in pastimes they could still do together. We encourage you to look for similar opportunities to have a good time. Your loved one will eventually become disabled by the disease, but you still have time to accomplish meaningful goals and enjoy life together. Mom received her diagnosis six years before she became so disabled that she and Dad had to move. Others have more time, but sadly, many have less.

You may have to resist the temptation to withdraw from social situations that used to be enjoyable. As Mom found formerly comfortable environments increasingly difficult, she pulled back. Dad withdrew also, too tired to be strong for both of them. He was weakened from the increasingly difficult job of taking care of Mom, and he didn't want to force her to do anything that made her even more uncomfortable than she already was. First Mom and then Dad avoided gatherings they used to enjoy. Soon, a chain reaction set in, as their acquaintances became uncertain of Mom's and Dad's wishes for phone calls and visits. The result was almost total isolation for our parents. We urge you not to let this happen to you; consider some of these suggestions:

- Invite friends over, but only one couple at a time.

- Plan activities with others during the Alzheimer's sufferer's "best hours."

- Attend community activities—concerts, plays, sporting events—sitting where you can leave early if necessary.

- Stay involved in your church.

Be creative and flexible. Focus on your abilities and those of your loved one. Replace the activities you're forced to give up with others of short duration and high interest. Make occasions out of everyday events. Answer the question "What can we still do together?"

Our parents found many things they could enjoy or accomplish as a couple in the early stages of the disease. Here are just a few ideas:

- Capture long-term memories. Interview each other on tape or CD.

- Play old familiar music.

- Visit places associated with pleasant memories from long ago. Ask others to take you if you can't drive.

- Be creative about finding ways to get out of the house— avoid isolation.

- Go through your belongings, disposing of or giving away as many unnecessary items as possible.

- Encourage all the members of your family to ask the important questions, have the important talks, and write the important letters while there's still time.

You should also make an effort to find tasks that the Alzheimer's sufferer can feel good about doing, such as:

- Working in the yard

- Setting the table

- Doing dishes

- Folding clothes

Caregivers can take a number of actions to make daily life safer, easier, and more comfortable for both themselves and their loved ones. Here are some changes to consider:

- Take control knobs off the stove.

- Check the kitchen frequently throughout the day and just before going to bed; make sure that all food is put away properly and appliances are turned off.

- Replace your answering machine with telephone company voice messaging and turn off the ringer when the person with Alzheimer's is home alone.

- Use a baby monitor at night.

- Hide a spare key outside the house.

- Check smoke alarms monthly.

- Lock up all medicines, alcohol, and guns.

- Secure smoking materials, ensuring that the Alzheimer's sufferer never smokes outside the presence of a caregiver.

> PROVERBS 27:23 NIV
>
> *Be sure you know the condition of your flocks,*
> *give careful attention to your herds;*

Alzheimer's sufferers and their families can still enjoy going out for a meal, but a few adjustments may make the experience more pleasant for everyone. Go early, choose a restaurant that offers quick service, and avoid buffets, which require too many decisions. As you enter the restaurant, you may want to inform the staff that your party has special needs. We did this frequently when dining with Mom, and people were always accommodating. (Cards that you can hand to servers for this purpose are available through the Alzheimer's Association.) Sit near the door and select a seat for your loved one that faces away from the distractions of the busy restaurant. Because menus may be more complicated than you realize, you may want to order for your loved one or offer just a couple of favorite selections to minimize frustration. Finally, ask for the check early to avoid a long wait at the end of the meal.

Alzheimer's sufferers frequently wander, putting themselves at great risk of getting lost, injured, or victimized. Consider the following actions:

- Put additional locks on doors or replace existing ones with more complicated models.

- Hide items that cue the person to go outside, such as coats, purses, hats, and boots.

- Alert neighbors to this potential problem, asking them to call the caregiver or guide the person with Alzheimer's home if they see your loved one wandering off.

- Enroll in the Alzheimer's Association Safe Return™ program, which provides an ID bracelet.

According to the Alzheimer's Association Western and Central Washington State Chapter, "Driving Safely," www.alzwa.org/ArticlesOnLine/Driving_Safety_Article/ driving_safety%202.htm, "Only 42 percent of persons with Alzheimer's stop driving before an accident occurs." We are aware of several studies that recommend that people do not drive once they are diagnosed with the disease. Watch for the following warning signs: fender benders or near misses, inability to find familiar places, problems interpreting signs, and/or driving citations.

As the caregiver, you need to make the hard decision at the very first sign of diminished capacity to prevent your loved one from driving. There are a number of actions you can take:

- Call the Alzheimer's patient's physician, asking for a prescription stating that the patient is no longer able to drive.

- Have your insurance company send the caregiver a letter stating that the sufferer's auto insurance coverage has been cancelled.

- Control access to the car keys.

- Have a mechanic install a "kill switch," preventing the person with Alzheimer's from starting the car.

Not only does driving become hazardous to your loved one and others, but allowing someone with Alzheimer's to drive may subject you to significant liability. This issue is emotionally charged, whether you are dealing with an Alzheimer's sufferer, a senior with failing eyesight, or anyone with diminished capacity. While you want to be compassionate and understanding of the loss this represents to your loved one, you must stand firm. Ask God to give you the words and the strength to help your loved one accept this difficult situation with His grace.

A Prayer

Heavenly Father, we praise You for Your goodness and mercy. You provide for our needs even before we are aware of them. Thank You for the gift of family, through whom You teach, guide, and support us. Help us to focus on what we can do and give us grace to let go of those things we can no longer do. Help us to walk with You rather than stumbling along on our own. Thy will be done. In Jesus' name, Amen.

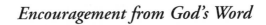

Encouragement from God's Word

ECCLESIASTES 3:1 NLT

There is a time for everything,
a season for every activity under heaven:

Additional Scriptures

PSALM 30:11–12 NIV

You turned my wailing into
dancing;
You removed my sackcloth and
clothed me with joy,
that my heart may sing to You and not
be silent.
O LORD my God, I will give You
thanks forever.

JOB 11:13, 15b–18a NIV

"Yet if you devote your heart to Him
and stretch out your hands to Him,
...you will stand firm and without fear.
You will surely forget your trouble,
recalling it only as waters gone by.
Life will be brighter than noonday,
and darkness will become like morning.
You will be secure, because there is hope..."

ROMANS 8:35, 37–39 NLT

Can anything ever separate us from Christ's love? Does it
mean He no longer loves us if we have trouble or calamity, or
are persecuted, or are hungry or cold or in danger or threat-
ened with death?...No, despite all these things, overwhelming
victory is ours through Christ, Who loved us.

And I am convinced that nothing can ever separate us from
His love. Death can't, and life can't. The angels can't, and the
demons can't. Our fears for today, our worries about tomor-
row, and even the powers of hell can't keep God's love away.

2 CORINTHIANS 4:6 NIV

For God, Who said, "Let light shine out of darkness," made
His light shine in our hearts to give us the light of the knowl-
edge of the glory of God in the face of Christ.

PHILIPPIANS 1:9–10 NIV

And this is my prayer: that your love may abound more and more in knowledge and depth of insight, so that you may be able to discern what is best and may be pure and blameless until the day of Christ,

JAMES 4:8 NIV

Come near to God and He will come near to you.

1 PETER 1:13 NIV

Therefore, prepare your minds for action; be self-controlled; set your hope fully on the grace to be given you when Jesus Christ is revealed.

Chapter 3: Primary Caregiver

Do I have the strength I'll need?

Our Story

> *"Hi, sisters; it's Ann. I got to Mom and Dad's this afternoon. They're both fine, although Dad seems really tired and maybe even a bit depressed."*

I was in Ripon to drive Mom and Dad to an out-of-town doctors' appointment and to get a feel for how things were going. Mom was aware of our concern and increased presence in their lives. Although she was happy to see and talk with us more regularly, she was also fearful of the inevitable loss of control her disease would bring to her life. She wanted their life together to stay just as it was, and she didn't want Dad discussing plans for their future with us. When we called, she made it a point to answer the phone, stay on the line, and control the conversation.

But Dad needed our help if he was going to take care of

Mom. Peggy and her daughter had visited several months earlier to set up a computer for Dad and teach him the basics of e-mailing and the Web. He was inquisitive by nature, and although he was in his 80s, he relished the opportunity to learn how to use a computer. It was impressive. That mode of communication had become essential because it allowed us to discuss issues with Dad that were worrisome and upsetting to Mom.

Even during my visit, Dad and I found little opportunity to talk alone. Running errands together or going for short walks offered the only uninterrupted and private times to discuss how Dad was dealing with Mom's Alzheimer's. When we were alone, I realized what a devastating effect Mom's illness was having on Dad's physical health.

> 2 CORINTHIANS 12:9a NIV
>
> *But He said to me, "My grace is sufficient for you, for My power is made perfect in weakness."*

I was looking forward to talking with the Alzheimer's specialists the next morning about the toll that Mom's illness was taking on Dad. When we arrived at the doctors' office, Dad was given a questionnaire to complete. He had told me ahead of time that he wanted me to fill it out because Mom would look over his shoulder if he did it. Not only was she becoming increasingly paranoid as the disease advanced, but I had a feeling Dad thought I would be more candid than he could bring himself to be. I was shocked when I discovered that filling out that form was his only semi-confidential opportunity to share his perspective on their situation with the people charged with treating Mom.

It was a grueling day for Mom. So many different doctors and nurses asked her unending questions, most of which she was unable to answer. Although the staff was friendly and tried to reassure her, she grew more and more tired, discouraged, and stressed.

We went from office to office, meeting with a variety of specialists. Mom was given one opportunity after another to share her opinions, but it wasn't until our last stop that someone finally asked Dad, "So, how do you think everything's going?" I looked at him, waiting for his answer. He was struggling. How could he tell the doctor what was really going on without hurting the woman he had loved for a lifetime?

I thought of all the things Dad and I had talked about: sleep deprivation, nutritional concerns, hygiene considerations, and a myriad of other problems that Dad was facing on a daily basis. All eyes were on him as he answered, "Well, cooking has become more difficult for Ruth, but we're managing." I knew that was the most Dad would be willing to say in front of Mom. I couldn't believe that he wouldn't get a chance to speak with the doctor in private.

Mom's exhaustion and frustration at the end of a long and excruciating day were palpable. It didn't surprise me when she immediately changed the topic of conversation to her garden. What did surprise me was that the doctor let it happen. He had asked Dad for his opinion. Why did he allow his Alzheimer's patient to prevent the caregiver from giving her doctor important information about their daily lives? If only he would have taken the initiative to meet with Dad privately, he would have gotten a much clearer picture of the progression of Mom's disease and its effect on their health and safety. Didn't he realize that by helping the caregiver he would also help the patient?

Mom's frustration with her difficulties in the kitchen turned to anger when Dad revealed the problem to the doctor. Her emotions surfaced as soon as we got out of the office and into the car. Dad was quiet the whole way home. When we finally arrived back in Ripon, Mom went up to bed. It had been an exhausting day for all of us.

Dad and I sat out on the back porch. "Dad, I can't believe how calm you stay when Mom gets upset. How do you do it?"

"Well, Ann, I focus on two things. First of all, I try to remember that it's the disease that's causing her anger. It's not your Mom. I love Ruth, and I always will. And then I pray for patience—over and over, all day long. It's the Lord Who's keeping me from saying anything I might regret."

> MATTHEW 11:28 NIV
>
> *"Come to Me, all you who are weary and burdened, and I will give you rest."*

Later that evening, I called Nancy and Peggy again to fill them in on the day. I felt that it was important to discuss the events with them before I forgot any of the details. We began to toss out ideas of what we could do the next time one of us went with Mom and Dad to see the doctor. We wanted to make sure that Dad would be able to give a more accurate picture of their situation on subsequent visits. He needed time alone with the doctor.

"Next time, let's be sure we make an opportunity to get Mom out of the room," Peggy suggested.

"I think one of us should call the doctors' office before their next visit," Nancy added. "Then we can alert the doctors to Dad's health issues and insist that they see him alone."

Talking with my sisters was helpful. Although we had missed this opportunity to get help for Dad, there would be others. Nancy and Peggy reminded me that we were still learning about Alzheimer's and we were doing the best we could.

Seeing firsthand how anxious and agitated Mom was becoming, observing Dad's declining health, and experiencing frustration at my inability to get help for Dad left me feeling depressed. I'd been face to face with the situation for only three days, but Dad lived it every day and every night. How was he going to survive? My heart ached for him.

As I lay in bed that night, I thought about how grateful I was that I was with Mom and Dad that day—how amazing that my calendar had been cleared at just the right time. I realized that God was calling my sisters and me to serve Him by more actively supporting our parents.

God, thank You for making it possible for me to be here, but I'm coming to You with a heavy heart. Dad is so tired and overwhelmed by Mom's illness. Give him strength and show us how to lift some of the burden from his shoulders. Give all of us patience and understanding when the symptoms of Alzheimer's are difficult to manage. Lord, we trust You and Your promise to be our refuge and strength—that You will always help us when we are in

PSALM 46:1 KJV

*God is our refuge and strength,
A very present help in trouble.*

trouble. I think we really are in trouble now. Show us Your will. In Jesus' name, Amen.

Your Guide

Alzheimer's affects the life of the caregiver 24 hours a day, but its changes are subtle and tend to sneak up on you. Without even realizing it, you are taking over more and more responsibility for tasks that your loved one is no longer able to complete.

We were all delighted when Dad started adding notes to birthday and anniversary cards. In retrospect, we could see the progression of his involvement in an area that had always been Mom's domain. First, he added short notes to Mom's letters; later, he wrote the notes and signed the cards himself; and still later, he was doing everything from buying the cards to addressing them and taking them to the post office. On our next visit, we could tell by the writing on the household calendar that the task of scheduling appointments and recognizing family birthdays and anniversaries had changed hands. Dad now had the full responsibility.

Shopping lists also switched from Mom's to Dad's handwriting, and for the first time in his life, Dad bought the groceries. He confided in us that he was learning to enjoy those trips but added that when Mom went with him, shopping was a lot harder because she took a long, long time and selected "rather exotic" items to place in their cart.

Although he never mastered the art of cooking, the kitchen became Dad's responsibility. Mom had always loved preparing meals for him but soon lost the ability to follow a recipe or stay focused on a task. Dad did his best to finish what she had begun, but safety issues with food preparation became a serious problem and were one of the factors that led to their eventual move.

Mom was unable to make a decision regarding the proper storage place for frozen or refrigerated items. Ice cream was found in the microwave, and meat was found in the cupboard. Mom couldn't figure out how much food to prepare for the two of them for a meal. The refrigerator would be filled with left-overs in various stages of "aging." She would prepare the same item day after day, forgetting that they had eaten it the day before. Mom could no longer determine which pots and pans went in the microwave for heating and which went on the stove.

In addition to assuming the day-to-day responsibilities of running the house, Dad was burdened by the clutter created by Mom's countless unfinished projects and her constant requests for assistance. She might have three or four projects going at once—trying to organize photographs in the family room, attempting to make Christmas ornaments on the kitchen table, sorting and resorting piles of clothes in the guest room—all in a seemingly desperate attempt to prove that she was still capable of accomplishing something.

Like our father, you may be experiencing greater and greater demands on your time and energy. Do an occasional self-inventory. Are you still tired when you get up in the

> **PSALM 6:2 NLT**
>
> *Have compassion on me, LORD, for I am weak. Heal me, LORD, for my body is in agony.*

morning? Do you feel overwhelmed by the thought of just getting through the day? Do you have enough energy to get done what has to be done today?

To provide the best possible care for your loved one, you need to take care of yourself. In light of your changing situation, we recommend that you schedule a personal appointment with your doctor. Ask for an extended-length appointment to give you and the doctor time to adequately address all your concerns. You may need to make more than one appointment. Confidentially and candidly discuss how your loved one's Alzheimer's is affecting you and have a thorough physical examination. If you don't think your doctor is taking these issues seriously, it is time to find a different doctor.

You may be hesitant to share details of the changes that are affecting your lives, but it is possible to discuss problems associated with Alzheimer's without being disrespectful to your loved one. You must relate how the disease is affecting your health and safety, specifically addressing:

- Stress
- Loss of sleep
- Inadequate diet

- Unsafe food handling
- Gas and electric hazards
- Deteriorating home cleanliness and maintenance
- Isolation and lack of personal space
- Frustration leading to anger
- Lack of time for exercise

The constant, daily stress, as well as the inherently irrational behavior of the person with Alzheimer's, often take their toll on the caregiver. Sometimes the stress, the lack of sleep, and the frustration can become overwhelming and surface in the form of hurtful or violent thoughts toward the patient. When this happens, it is a sign that help is needed immediately.

If you don't take care of yourself, you can't take care of your loved one. Lack of sleep is a major problem. When sleep loss begins to affect your strength, health, or emotional well-being, you might consider one of the following options:

- Make an appointment with a physician to determine if medication for one or both of you would be helpful.

- Enroll your loved one in adult day care and take advantage of the opportunity to rest.

- Avail yourself of hourly drop-off day-care services, sometimes offered by retirement homes or senior centers, to allow yourself time for a quick nap.

- Ask for volunteers or hire someone to occupy your loved one while you sleep.

- Join an Alzheimer's support group to benefit from the

experience of others. (Check with your state chapter of the Alzheimer's Association.)

> ISAIAH 40:29, 31 NIV
>
> *He gives strength to the weary*
> *and increases the power of the weak...*
> *but those who hope in the LORD*
> *will renew their strength.*
> *They will soar on wings like eagles;*
> *they will run and not grow weary,*
> *they will walk and not be faint.*

• Move your loved one to a nearby specialized facility offering round-the-clock care.

In retrospect, we three daughters should have been more consistently involved in our parents' living conditions earlier in the course of the disease. Mom and Dad's situation deteriorated rapidly without our knowledge. Like many families today, we were spread across the country, from Virginia to Texas, with our parents in Wisconsin. We read articles on Alzheimer's, called frequently to see how things were going, made occasional quick trips home, and convinced ourselves that nothing much had changed.

What we didn't do was make it a point to spend a week with Mom and Dad at their home occasionally. We should have assessed the situation with them periodically and responded promptly to the problems they were facing as the disease progressed.

Dad needed a lot more assistance than he received. It just wasn't his nature to share personal problems or ask for help.

We believe this is true of many primary caregivers. We encourage family and friends to offer help and spend time with people living with Alzheimer's, even if, from the outside, the situation appears to be under control.

Each of us could have taken a more active role. We came to regret that we had not visited our parents more often and for longer periods of time during the early stages of the disease. We could have seen for ourselves what was happening. Once we realized the need, we were able to share the burden. Our support not only made life easier for our parents but also gave each us of an opportunity to grow into a new and deeper relationship with Dad and with the Lord.

Although asking for help was hard for Dad in those early years, he eventually understood that being able to assist our parents was a blessing to us. As he realized how much we loved doing things for them, asking for help became easier for him. As the primary caregiver, reach out to your family and friends for help and support. Give them an opportunity to serve God by helping you.

A Prayer

Heavenly Father, thank You for Your comforting presence. How reassuring it is to know that You are present everywhere at all times so that we are not alone on this difficult and dark journey. Thank You for placing us in families, so that we can support and encourage one another. Lord, we ask that You continue to give us patience, guidance, and strength to walk in the light of Your love. Thy will be done. In Jesus' name, Amen.

Courage from God's Word

ISAIAH 41:10 NIV

So do not fear, for I am with you;
do not be dismayed, for I am your God.
I will strengthen you and help you;
I will uphold you with My righteous right hand.

Additional Scriptures

PSALM 62:8 NIV

Trust in Him at all times, O people;
pour out your hearts to Him,
for God is our refuge.

PSALM 63:6–8 NLT

I lie awake thinking of You,
meditating on You through the night.
I think how much You have helped me;
I sing for joy in the shadow of Your protecting wings.
I follow close behind You;
Your strong right hand holds me securely.

PSALM 121:1–3 NIV

I lift up my eyes to the hills—
  where does my help come from?
My help comes from the LORD,
  the Maker of heaven and earth.

He will not let your foot slip—
  He Who watches over you will not slumber.

MICAH 7:7, 8b NIV

But as for me, I watch in hope for the LORD,
  I wait for God my Savior;
  my God will hear me.

Though I sit in darkness,
  the LORD will be my light.

PHILIPPIANS 4:13 NIV

I can do everything through Him Who gives me strength.

COLOSSIANS 4:2, 6 NLT

  Devote yourselves to prayer with an alert mind and a
thankful heart.

Let your conversation be gracious and effective so that you will
have the right answer for everyone.

JAMES 1:12 NIV

  Blessed is the man who perseveres under trial, because
when he has stood the test, he will receive the crown of life that
God has promised to those who love Him.

Chapter 4: Sources of Support

Where can I go for help?

Our Story

> "*Hi, this is Nance. I've been with Mom and Dad for almost ten days, and the situation has really deteriorated since you were here, Ann. I think the three of us need to spend a week in Ripon together as soon as possible. When can you come?*"

We were able to rearrange our work schedules and take advantage of the Fourth of July weekend to spend a week together with Mom and Dad. For almost half a century, they'd lived happily in the 150-year-old colonial home, gray with green shutters. Their marriage was as close to storybook perfect as any couple can get.

Handsome, soon-to-be professional young man meets beautiful sorority coed. They fall in love, marry, and have three healthy baby girls. He builds a successful business while she creates a lovely home for them.

They raise their daughters to adulthood, and the girls marry and present them with a gaggle of grandchildren.

Mom and Dad had always agreed on almost everything, until Dad started looking into retirement communities. He was convinced they would offer an easier, fuller life for both of them. Mom opposed each and every alternative he presented. It soon became apparent that she wasn't just being fussy; she simply didn't want to move.

Mom had lived her entire life in Wisconsin and most of her adult life in Ripon. She truly loved the small town and the beautiful rolling farmland that encircled it. She and Dad were surrounded by friends and acquaintances in Ripon, although as is often the case with seniors, most of their closest friends had either died or moved to retirement communities in other places that were nearer their children. Mom's earlier desire to stay near her friends had been replaced by a fear of leaving familiar surroundings. Even in her own community, even in the home she'd lived in for more than 40 years, life was becoming confusing. How could she ever adapt to a strange home in a strange town?

Dad knew Mom's fear had become the motivation behind her aversion to moving. He had given up the fight. We agreed with Dad that life would probably be better for them elsewhere, but it was, after all, *their* decision. We simply wanted to help make staying where they were as comfortable and safe as possible for them. Therefore, our goal for this visit was to secure in-home help for our parents.

After Mom and Dad went to bed, the three of us sat on the

screened-in porch. The gentle breeze and soft sounds of the summer evening were in sharp contrast to the harsh realities of Dad's rapidly failing health and Mom's increased confusion. We asked God to guide us in finding skilled help for the parents we love so much. We decided to start our search by visiting their pastor the next morning, right after our appointment with Dad's lawyer.

EPHESIANS 3:20 NLT

Now glory be to God! By His mighty power at work within us, He is able to accomplish infinitely more than we would ever dare to ask or hope.

Because we had a lot to do, we headed out early the next day for our meeting at the lawyer's downtown office. Dad had arranged for us to sign durable powers of attorney for him and Mom, along with several other legal documents. The attorney lived across the street from our folks, yet he was surprised to learn how far Mom's disease had advanced. Theirs was a friendly neighborhood, and we couldn't believe he was unaware of her condition. This was the first of many encounters we had with people whom we would have expected to know Mom's condition but didn't.

Dad would never knowingly do anything that was disrespectful of Mom. He was doing a good job of keeping their problems private. In doing so, he was also keeping people from reaching out to help them.

From the attorney's office, we walked over to the church and had a few minutes to visit with the secretary before our meeting with the pastor. We told her that we were looking for help for our parents, and she related that church members had seen signs of Mom's confusion and were concerned. She suggested we contact Sharon, a nurse in town who had recently retired from providing services to the elderly of Fond du Lac County. When the secretary mentioned Sharon's last name, we looked at each other in amazement. She was the wife of Dad's former business partner and a dear family friend. We saw God's hand at work. He was clearly leading us. Sharon was the perfect person with the perfect talents, coming to us at the perfect time.

> JEREMIAH 29:11 NIV
>
> *"For I know the plans I have for you," declares the LORD, "plans to prosper you and not to harm you, plans to give you hope and a future."*

Sharon and her husband, Bob, knew about Mom's illness and had already reached out to help our parents. On more than one occasion, they had asked Dad, "Is there anything we can do for you and Ruth?"

Dad's answer was always the same: "Oh, thanks, but we're doing fine."

We were relieved that Sharon was able to see us that afternoon. She ushered us into their beautiful sunroom, and we immediately relaxed in the warmth of her home and her friendship. Sharon got right to the point: "I was so glad to hear from you girls. We've been trying to find out what we can do to help your folks. How are they doing?"

Although Dad had difficulty opening up about the situation, he had readily agreed that we should be candid with

Sharon. He realized they needed help.

Having his permission, we described our concerns—Mom's confusion, Dad's deteriorating health, the stove being left on, food not being refrigerated, inadequate nutrition, sleepless nights, increasing isolation, depression, hygiene issues.... We concluded by asking Sharon to help us find in-home help for our parents.

She replied, "With what you've just described, there's no way your folks can stay there. It's just not safe."

Wow! Here was a knowledgeable, trusted friend telling us that our goal for this visit was unrealistic. The new reality was that we had to find a safer home for our parents. Although we knew they would have to move eventually, we were shocked that they were already at that point. It took the objective advice of a caring professional to enable us to face the situation head on.

The three of us had talked long into the night, so we were surprised to find Nancy heading out the door at 8:00 the next morning. She explained that during her early morning quiet time, she had felt a compelling need to go to the church. Because we were all learning to follow the promptings of the Holy Spirit, Nancy got ready and headed up the hill, arriving moments before Sharon. We had asked both Sharon and the pastor to get in touch with each other, but we had no idea they would respond so quickly. God's perfect timing...

> GALATIANS 5:25 NLT
>
> *If we are living now by the Holy Spirit, let us follow the Holy Spirit's leading in every part of our lives.*

Nancy was amazed: "I didn't expect to see both of you here."

Sharon was quick to respond, "We both felt God was calling us to help. Your parents can't stay in that home any longer, Nancy. It's dangerous. I've seen cases in my work where people waited too long, where inaction led to tragedy."

"I guess we should have realized…We're so grateful for your help, both of you. You know, I really think Dad needs to be here." Nancy called home to arrange for him to come up to the church.

We had talked with Dad after our meeting with Sharon the day before, and he was in full agreement with our change in direction. In fact, he was relieved to finally make the decision, eager to make the move. The pastor and Sharon pledged to support our family in this crisis, and we went away from the meeting knowing that God had brought us two willing helpers. Dad's support team was growing.

Your Guide

The caregiver's job is too big for one person. In addition to handling the increasing day-to-day responsibilities, many life-altering decisions must be made. If you suspect that your loved one has Alzheimer's, don't put off speaking to family members, clergy, and friends who are apt to be helpful. You may think that keeping the disease private is in the best interests of your loved one, but the opposite is true. In fact, people who are removed from the situation may be able to see solutions more clearly. Just make sure you select people whose judgment and discretion you trust.

Form a support team to assist you in making decisions. These people will share the burden and pray for you. The three of us were the first members of Dad's team, but it soon became obvious that he needed more support from people with diverse skills. As we moved along on this journey, some people were intimately involved every step of the way. Others provided essential support for shorter periods of time. Altogether, dozens of people directly supported Dad, each with a unique and vital role.

Family formed the foundation of Dad's support structure. We brought varied skills and knowledge to the effort. The fact that we are spread across the country did not prevent us from being the primary members of Dad's team. Modern forms of communication (cell phones, e-mail, facsimiles, and overnight delivery) kept us connected with Dad and with one another.

As needs arose, God added people to the team—Mom and Dad's pastor, church members, business associates, and neighbors—old friends and new.

> ROMANS 12:6a, 7a, 8a NIV
>
> *We have different gifts, according to the grace given us....If it is serving, let him serve...if it is encouraging, let him encourage; if it is contributing to the needs of others, let him give generously...*

They came to Mom and Dad's aid in different ways: Some were sought out to assist with specific needs; others approached us with offers of help; several, we "happened" to run into at just the right time; and many came to mind as we sought guidance from the Holy Spirit.

Your church family can and should be a source of support of many kinds, including praying for your needs. Many churches set aside time in the service for people to voice specific prayers or for the pastor to lead the congregation in praying for individual needs of the members. If you as the caregiver and the Alzheimer's sufferer agree, having the church family pray for both of you can be helpful in many ways:

- Members become aware of your needs and may offer help and support to relieve you or minister directly to your loved one.

- Members are given the opportunity to grow closer to God by praying for you.

- The prayers of others serve as a reminder that God is present in every situation.

God is your guide on this journey. He is always with you, and His plan is perfect. He already knows the path you are to take. As we sought help for Dad, God answered our prayers by providing willing people with just the right skills. God placed the perfect people, with the perfect talents, at the perfect time into our totally imperfect situation. God will answer your prayers, too.

Our experience reconnecting with Sharon was just one of many in which people with special talents seemed to find us precisely when we needed them. One of the most amazing of these experiences involved the pastor at our parents' church. Their long-time minister had retired, leaving a vacancy in the pulpit. The church hierarchy had assigned an interim pastor. He and his wife had become close friends of Mom and Dad. Although the church had appointed him, we are convinced his selection came from God.

The pastor was one of the first people to join us in Dad's support team and was with our parents every step of the way until they left Ripon for the last time. As we reflected on the vital role he played in keeping us in God's will, helping Mom accept assistance she so desperately needed, and giving Dad a mission for the future, we feel certain that our parents' lives would have been permanently and negatively affected had he not been leading their church community during our crisis. It is impossible to convince us that his presence in our lives was anything but a gift from God.

As Alzheimer's becomes more prevalent, numerous organizations are rallying to support families affected by the disease. We recommend that you find out about social services available through your local, county, or state government. Commercial providers of home health care and other services are also available in many communities.

The Internet and your local library are excellent resources for keeping abreast of recent developments in Alzheimer's treatment, as well as information on related services (see appendix). If you don't have time to tap into these sources yourself, you probably have a friend or acquaintance who would be willing to assist you. Many young people are experienced with the World Wide Web. Perhaps you have a grandchild who could be recruited to help you with this project. Be creative and assertive as you seek help.

> HEBREWS 6:10 NIV
>
> *God is not unjust; He will not forget your work and the love you have shown Him as you have helped His people and continue to help them.*

As you identify the people who are willing and able to support you in your role of caregiver, you should start matching them up with the types of help you need. Ask yourself the following questions:

- Is housekeeping a problem? Hire a service or inquire at your church about potential volunteers. Have a friend take the person with Alzheimer's out for a few hours to free you up to take care of the cleaning. Scout troops, sororities, and fraternities are often looking for service projects; consider contacting one of these groups about this or other needs.

- Are you having trouble preparing nutritious meals? Many communities offer a solution to this problem through Meals on Wheels; church ministries may also provide this service. When friends ask what they can do to help, suggest that they prepare a meal. Keep your own cooking simple and double your recipes, freezing half for a rainy day. Check out some of the frozen dinners available at your neighborhood grocery store.

- Do you need help with transportation? Don't be shy about asking for rides when people offer assistance. Find out about reduced rates and special provisions for seniors. Request papers for free ride services from the patient's doctor. Arrange to tag along on a neighbor's shopping trip. Ask a church member to pick you up on the way to services.

- Are you feeling overwhelmed by challenges associated with Alzheimer's, such as the patient's wandering, incontinence, tantrums, inability to bathe, or insistence on driving? Find tips on how to deal with specific issues on the Alzheimer's Association Web site or call the association's toll-free number (see appendix). You might also consider joining an Alzheimer's support group to learn how others in the same situation are handling these issues.

- Does the Alzheimer's sufferer need help with personal care? Ask your physician to refer you to a good home health-care agency or similar service. Close, loving friends or family members are also good candidates for this kind of assistance.

We can't remember a single incident when we asked for help and it was not given willingly. Occasionally, the help came in the form of a referral to a better resource. You probably know many people who are waiting for an opportunity to lend you a hand, and you should allow them to do so. Don't force yourself to carry this burden alone.

Our faith increased as we experienced God's provision for our specific needs time after time. Give your needs to the Lord in prayer and wait for Him to bring someone to your mind or maybe even to your doorstep. He will provide.

Although this chapter focuses on the support team for the caregiver, many of the suggestions we offer will also help the person afflicted with Alzheimer's. Both caregivers and their loved ones may find that the simple gift of time is one of the most valuable offerings that those who wish to help can give. Perhaps a friend, neighbor, or younger relative can visit the Alzheimer's sufferer to play simple games or work easy puzzles together, make a batch of cookies, take a walk, help send cards to friends and relatives, or just talk about the past before those memories are gone forever.

In fact, providing an opportunity for the person with Alzheimer's to talk about an earlier time is a wonderful gift. These older memories seem to be more accessible, and reliving them can be pleasant and comforting. The Alzheimer's sufferer can contribute to the conversation without the anxiety that is becoming more common in their interaction with others.

> 1 THESSALONIANS 5:11 NIV
>
> *Therefore encourage one another and build each other up...*

Many communities have services that provide paid companions, but you probably have people in your network of friends who would be willing to assist you in this way. If possible, find those who are able to commit to a regular schedule of visits, but also encourage others to call on your loved one. Often people would like to stop in but hesitate to do so without getting an invitation.

Adult day care is becoming available in more communities. The environment is non-threatening, and many seniors enjoy participating in activities geared to their special needs. The challenge lies in convincing the Alzheimer's sufferer to go for the first one or two visits. After trying the experience a couple of times, many people love it. If you are meeting resistance, present adult day care as a way to help the caregiver or as an opportunity to help others who are attending.

We can't repeat this point often enough: You must take care of yourself if you're going to be able to take care of your loved one. Take advantage of opportunities to do something for yourself—go for a walk, go shopping, visit friends, take a nap. Reward yourself for the hard work you've been doing and your faithful service to your loved one.

Finally, you should meet regularly with a good listener, someone who truly cares about what's happening in your life. Dad had such a friend in Charlie, his neighbor of more than 40 years. The two of them would visit almost daily, Charlie making his way across the street to see how the folks were doing. After Charlie passed away, his daughter, Lee, took over for her father. Because she lived in the country, her visits were less frequent, but they were regular—something Dad could count on to break up the routine and the isolation that was closing in on them.

Lee had been helping our parents for quite a while, and her participation in their support team was to last for a long time.

We called on her for a variety of tasks, and she was always a willing helper—driving Mom and Dad up to the cottage, helping them with jobs around the house, coordinating with workmen when repairs needed to be done. She is not only a very capable person but a loving one, and someone with whom they both felt comfortable. She was often the perfect person to support Mom and Dad.

> JOB 2:11 NIV
>
> *When Job's three friends… heard about all the troubles that had come upon him, they set out from their homes and met together by agreement to go and sympathize with him and comfort him.*

Like her father, Lee had a sincere interest in Mom and Dad's well-being. Although the purpose of her visits was always to support her father's friend, we suspect that their time together was a mutual blessing. As she ministered to our parents, Dad helped to fill the void left by the loss of her father. This was the beginning of Lee's involvement on Dad's support team, and her assistance became even more important in the difficult weeks surrounding our parents' relocation.

A Prayer

Heavenly Father, You are our Shepherd and our Guide. Thank You for leading us on this journey and for providing all the people and resources we need along the way. Help us to seek and graciously accept the assistance of others. Keep us in fellowship with You and with each other. Thy will be done. In Jesus' name, Amen.

Counsel from God's Word

ECCLESIASTES 4:9–10 NIV

Two are better than one,
because they have a good return for their work:
If one falls down,
his friend can help him up.
But pity the man who falls
and has no one to help him up!

Additional Scriptures

PROVERBS 11:25 NIV

A generous man will prosper;
he who refreshes others will himself be refreshed.

PROVERBS 17:17 NLT

A friend is always loyal, and a brother is born to help in time of need.

ECCLESIASTES 4:12b NIV

A cord of three strands is not quickly broken.

MATTHEW 18:20 KJV

For where two or three are gathered together in My name, there am I in the midst of them.

MATTHEW 25:40 KJV

And the King shall answer and say unto them, Verily I say unto you, Inasmuch as ye have done it unto one of the least of these My brethren, ye have done it unto Me.

JOHN 14:6a, 16–17a NLT

Jesus told him... "And I will ask the Father, and He will give you another Counselor, Who will never leave you. He is the Holy Spirit, Who leads into all truth...."

EPHESIANS 2:10 NKJV

For we are His workmanship, created in Christ Jesus for good works, which God prepared beforehand that we should walk in them.

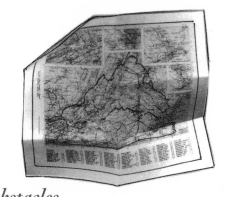

Chapter 5: Adjusting to Change and Overcoming Obstacles

Where do we go from here?

Our Story

> *"Hi, Hal. It's Peg. I've got something for the top of your honey-do list. We'd like you to check out some possible retirement communities in Virginia."*

Once Dad made the decision to move, we promised to take care of every detail. We continued to be concerned about his health, and he was grateful that he could rely on us.

Knowing the move would be extremely upsetting to Mom, we decided to wait as long as possible before telling her. We "ran a lot of errands" and took Nancy's golden retriever on some very long walks while talking long distance with candidate retirement communities for Mom and Dad.

Because Nancy and Peggy both lived in northern Virginia, we decided to look for a retirement community there. We knew the importance of having our parents near family, where they would have frequent visits from children, grandchildren, and great grandchildren.

Peggy's husband, Hal, had been busy checking out possibilities in Virginia and was keeping us informed by cell phone.

"Peg. This is Hal. I think we're down to two possibilities—one in Charlottesville and one out in the country."

"Okay. Is there any chance you could drive out to the country this afternoon? We really need to make a decision, and we've already seen the other one."

"No problem. I'll call you from there."

Later that afternoon, the three of us drove over to the church to update the pastor on the two places we were considering for the move. The pastor's closing prayer ended with this request: "Lord, we want to do Your will. If we are going in the wrong direction, please close the door and send us down another path."

PROVERBS 20:24a NIV

A man's steps are directed by the LORD.

We didn't wait long for God's response. When we got in the car to leave the church, Peggy's cell phone rang. It was Hal. "Hi, Peg. I'm afraid I've got bad news for you. I just got off the phone, and Charlottesville is no longer an option. They don't have any openings for at least six months. I'm just going into the other place; I'll call you when I'm finished."

We drove over to the millpond and sat on a park bench facing the water. It was a moment of tranquility in an otherwise

The strength of Dad's faith was a blessing, and it would soon be tested. Not long after we returned to our homes, a person who had not seen our parents for decades, knew nothing about the situation, and had never been close to the family confronted Dad about planning to move Mom from her home. Making the decision to move had been one of the hardest things he had ever done, and now this virtual stranger was telling him he was making a mistake. Dad was devastated. We were concerned and upset by her inappropriate intrusion.

Because we were not in Wisconsin during this vulnerable time for Dad, we called our cousin Chuck. His mother had cared for his father before his death from Alzheimer's. He had seen the ravages of the disease and knew firsthand what was in Mom and Dad's best interest. We asked Chuck if he would call Dad to reassure him that the decision he had made was the right one. He responded by writing Dad a beautiful letter that not only repaired the damage but also bolstered Dad's spirits.

Chuck was the perfect person at the perfect time with the perfect response.

> PROVERBS 12:18 NIV
>
> *Reckless words pierce like a sword,*
> *but the tongue of the wise brings healing.*

Your Guide

When Alzheimer's strikes your family, the changes you will experience are dramatic and unavoidable. You can generally meet these challenges in one of three ways. Some people will do nothing until forced to respond immediately to a crisis. Others will be able to make small adjustments over time as the disease progresses (see chapter 4). Still others will come quickly to a decision to move to an environment that is better equipped to handle Alzheimer's. This may involve moving in with a family member or relocating the sufferer to a facility that cares for Alzheimer's patients.

For us, the change began with a crisis when we returned to Ripon and realized our parents could no longer remain safely in their home. We made some adjustments to hold them over while we planned for a move. If you don't have to relocate as quickly as our parents did, we suggest that you continually reevaluate your situation. Ask members of your support team to assist you in this process. They may be helpful in objectively assessing your needs and suggesting options that fit your financial resources.

A retirement community near family was the best option for our parents. They would once again have safe, nutritious meals. They would be near family members who could provide ongoing support for anything they needed. They would no longer be isolated but would have a social life with people their own age who would understand their circumstances. Their neighborhood would be quieter, with less traffic and round-the-clock security. Help would be available at the push of a button. They would be relieved of the responsibilities of housekeeping and yard work. Just having a smaller home would make our parents' day-to-day existence less complicated.

Although our parents' quality of life would improve dramatically with their move, the transition would have been easier for Mom if it had occurred much earlier. Even in their home in Ripon, Mom was experiencing confusion. In their new home, things would be even more disorienting for her. The light switches and telephone would have to be found again and again. She might get turned around going to the bathroom or bedroom. The adjustment could have been much easier and quicker if they had moved when Dad first started talking about the possibility. Nonetheless, the move was essential for their safety.

If you believe that a retirement community will be your ultimate destination, consider making the change as soon as possible. The sooner relocation to a retirement community occurs, the smoother the adjustment will be. You will have time to enjoy new friends, good food, and fun activities—a renewed social life. Many of these communities offer laundry and housekeeping services, transportation, access to medical services, indoor and outdoor maintenance, security, and sensitivity to the needs of seniors.

Over the past several years, we have talked with many people in retirement communities, and not one of them has ever said that the move was premature. On the contrary, many expressed regret that they hadn't made the move years earlier.

Our family quickly agreed on a course of action for the move. More important, we shared a common desire to act in accordance with God's will, actively seeking His guidance and following His plan for our parents. We were united in putting aside our personal agendas because we knew God had the answer for our family.

Of course, not all families are able to come together in times of crisis. In fact, the fabric of a family can be torn apart as members argue or refuse to make the compromises or sacrifices required to reach agreement. For those of you who are struggling to come to a consensus on what's best for your

loved ones, we urge you to give the problem to God in prayer. Take advantage of wise counselors. Put aside your personal motives and focus on what is best for the Alzheimer's sufferer and the primary caregiver.

> ROMANS 14:19 NIV
>
> *Let us therefore make every effort to do what leads to peace...*

Because we were in agreement, we were able to deal effectively with outside opposition to the move. People may object to decisions you make regarding your future and that of your loved one. These negative opinions can come from a variety of sources—family, friends, neighbors, acquaintances, church members, business associates, relative strangers, service providers (legal, financial, or insurance professionals), even misguided medical personnel. Opposition may be based on a variety of factors:

- Sincere differences of opinion that should be considered

- Inability to be objective because of personal fears that those in opposition may someday face the same crisis

- Vested interests, particularly financial

- Lack of knowledge

- Power struggle or control issues within the family

- Curiosity or interference from neighbors or acquaintances

- Guilt from a lack of previous involvement

If you are secure in your decision and you know it's based on the best interests of the sufferer and the caregiver, don't let opposition prevent you from taking the right action.

Dad turned the responsibility for finding the right home over to the three of us. We knew that their new residence would have to offer both independent living and the Alzheimer's unit that Mom would eventually need. Having our parents close to other family members was essential to encourage and enable frequent visits. We wanted a Christian affiliation, a place with a friendly staff and residents who obviously enjoyed living there. Also important were good food and a pleasant dining experience, activities for each of our parents, and housekeeping and other services to make their lives easier and safer. Nancy's daughter, a nurse with experience in Alzheimer's care, advised us that a stable staff with low turn-

> ISAIAH 48:17b NIV
>
> *"I am the LORD your God,*
> *Who teaches you what is best for you,*
> *Who directs you in the way you should go...."*

over is one indication of a well-run facility, and our observations have convinced us that this is true.

In visiting retirement communities, make sure you scrutinize the Alzheimer's unit, even if your need for it is not immediate (see chapter 9). When we were looking for communities for Mom and Dad, we were grateful that Mom wouldn't need to live in an Alzheimer's unit right away. Nonetheless, we wanted to make sure that when she did make that move, the facility would be safe and well-staffed with competent, caring professionals.

Candidate facilities should be clean, fresh, and cheerful. You should see an adequate number of staff members interacting with and attending to the needs of patients. Look for residents who are relaxed and being attended to, not sitting alone in their rooms. Ask about the Alzheimer's care training program. In our experience, specialized training greatly enhances the living environment for the patients. Alzheimer's disease has unique symptoms, and its caregivers need training beyond basic geriatric care.

Deciding to relocate is a major decision. It's worth investing the time to make multiple visits to potential residences, at random times, with and without appointments. Doing so will give you a more complete picture of the new environment you're choosing.

We started this journey without a clear view of our destination, but we had asked God, "Where do we go from here?" and He showed us the way. He wants to be your guide, too.

> ISAIAH 58:11a NIV
>
> *"The LORD will guide you always..."*

A Prayer

Heavenly Father, we come to You for wisdom and guidance.
Thank You for Your gift of the Bible that lights our path.
Please direct our thoughts, words, and actions so that we main-
tain unity of purpose. Help all of us adjust to the changes
Alzheimer's disease has forced on our lives. Thy will be done.
In Jesus' name, Amen.

A Petition from God's Word

PSALM 143:8 NIV

*Let the morning bring me word of Your unfailing love,
for I have put my trust in You.
Show me the way I should go,
for to You I lift up my soul.*

Additional Scriptures

PSALM 20:4 NIV

*May He give you the desire of your heart
and make all your plans succeed.*

PSALM 119:105 NIV

*Your Word is a lamp to my feet
and a light for my path.*

PROVERBS 2:6–11 NIV

> *For the LORD gives wisdom,*
> *and from His mouth come knowledge and understanding.*
> *He holds victory in store for the upright,*
> *He is a shield to those whose walk is blameless,*
> *for He guards the course of the just*
> *and protects the way of His faithful ones.*
>
> *Then you will understand what is right and just*
> *and fair—every good path.*
> *For wisdom will enter your heart,*
> *and knowledge will be pleasant to your soul.*
> *Discretion will protect you,*
> *and understanding will guard you.*

PROVERBS 16:3 NIV

> *Commit to the LORD whatever you do,*
> *and your plans will succeed.*

NAHUM 1:7 NIV

> *The LORD is good,*
> *a refuge in times of trouble.*
> *He cares for those who trust in Him...*

LUKE 11:9–10 NIV

> *"So I say to you: Ask and it will be given to you; seek and you will find; knock and the door will be opened to you. For everyone who asks receives; he who seeks finds; and to him who knocks, the door will be opened...."*

ACTS 17:26–28 NIV

"From one man He made every nation of men, that they should inhabit the whole earth; and He determined the times set for them and the exact places where they should live. God did this so that men would seek Him and perhaps reach out for Him and find Him, though He is not far from each one of us. 'For in Him we live and move and have our being.'…"

Chapter 6: Handling Resistance

How can I be a peacemaker?

Our Story

"Nance, we have a problem."

It was a call from Dad. In spite of our best efforts to protect her, Mom had found out about Dad's plans to move them to a retirement community in Virginia. She was hysterical and had gone running out the front door. Dad was going after her but made a quick call to alert us to the crisis.

We had developed a detailed plan that included telling Mom just before the move. We hoped the delay would spare her weeks of needless worry. Years before, Dad had taken her to see several retirement communities. Although she would initially appear to be open to the idea of moving, she never really was. She loved Wisconsin. She had never lived anywhere else. Her home was comfortable, and it was safe...or so she thought. Indeed, her home had been safe, but it wasn't any longer.

Alzheimer's was making life so confusing for Mom. She couldn't remember people's names. She couldn't carry on an extended conversation. She couldn't even remember to take a shower. How could she leave the home she knew and loved and survive anywhere else?

Dad knew Mom didn't want to move and understood her fears. He had loved her from the first moment he saw her, and he loved making her happy. But now he was more than her husband; he was also her primary caregiver. He knew their home was no longer the safe haven she thought it was.

> ECCLESIASTES 8:5–6 NIV
>
> *Whoever obeys His command will come to no harm,*
>   *and the wise heart will know the proper time and*
>   *procedure.*
> *For there is a proper time and procedure for every*
>   *matter,*
>   *though a man's misery weighs heavily upon him.*

We had promised Dad that we would handle all the details of the move. One of the first details we discussed was the schedule. With Dad's call to Nancy, our carefully planned timetable went out the window. She set up a conference call for the three of us.

"Ann and Peg, I just got a call from Dad. Mom knows about the move. We need to get to Ripon right away. How soon can you leave?"

Ann responded, "I can't believe this happened. You're right; we need to go. I'm sure I can get a flight this evening and be there by 10:00."

"Good, I know Dad will be relieved to have one of us get there tonight," Peggy commented. "I can leave the office right away and be on the road in a couple of hours. How about you, Nance?"

"Same here. I'll pick you up about 3:00—4:00 at the latest. But before we hang up, let's say a quick prayer.

"Lord, calm our hearts. Thank You for being with us. We know You have control over the situation; help us to follow Your lead. Please be with Mom and Dad and help us get to them safely and quickly. Thy will be done. In Jesus' name, Amen.

NUMBERS 6:24–26 KJV

The LORD bless thee, and keep thee:
The LORD make His face shine upon thee, and
be gracious unto thee:
The LORD lift up His countenance upon thee, and
give thee peace.

"I feel better already. Our Heavenly Father is truly amazing. I can't believe we can all be on our way so fast."

In a matter of hours, the three of us were headed to Mom and Dad's, a week before our original schedule. We would stay with them until they were fully settled in their new home.

Mom was at the door when we arrived, asking, "Just why are you girls here?" This was not going to be a happy family reunion.

We spent the next two weeks trying to convince Mom that this move was in her best interests. We were pulled into an endless cycle of explanations of why the move was necessary, countered by Mom's inability to accept the reality of the situation and her fears, expressed as anger. These conversations were followed by a period of relative calm when Mom forgot everything we'd discussed.

Although we had a false start, we were anxious to return to our detailed plan. Determined to convince Mom that the move was in her best interests, we had set up a meeting for Sunday after church, again calling on Dad's support team to help. Our cousin Chuck, a favorite of Mom's, had agreed to join us. As we all moved into the pastor's office, everyone except Mom sat down in the seats he offered. Mom ignored his invitation to be seated, choosing instead to pace back and forth in front of the window that overlooked the millpond.

> PROVERBS 19:21 NIV
>
> *Many are the plans in a man's heart,*
> *but it is the LORD's purpose that prevails.*

Even the pastor's heartfelt opening prayer didn't relieve the tension in the room, and the meeting went downhill from there. Each of us took a turn relating the benefits of moving to Mom. She remained aloof and disconnected. The meeting did not go according to *our* plan.

After Mom and Dad were in bed that night, we sat on the back porch and reflected on what had gone wrong. We realized that we had not sought God's counsel in developing this part of the plan. We were following our plan, not God's.

"I can't believe how hard that meeting was for all of us, but especially for Mom and Dad. Mom seemed so frightened and angry." Peggy was fighting back tears.

Nancy said, "I'll never forget Dad's reaction when the pastor asked Mom, 'Do you love Al enough to go with him wherever he goes?' Dad was sitting bent over, resting his forearms on his knees. He had his head down. He may have even had his eyes closed."

> GENESIS 2:24 KJV
>
> *Therefore shall a man leave his father and his mother, and shall cleave unto his wife: and they shall be one flesh.*

"You're right. That's exactly what he looked like. I think he was probably praying," Ann added.

Peggy went on, sobbing openly now, her words coming in breathless, choking phrases: "Dad lifted his head and looked at Mom. His eyes were pleading. He wanted her to say yes so much. If she would say it, he would know that she was still the woman who had said yes so many years ago. Things were going to be okay. But she only said, 'I do love Al, but I don't want to move.'"

Mom's reaction was purely emotional, based on fear and confusion. She needed our love and support, not a sales pitch that would be forgotten almost immediately. The rest of us knew that the decision to move was the right one—indeed, the only one. We wanted her not merely to accept the move but to look forward to it, to be excited and anticipate an easier and safer life.

We should have known that was impossible. Mom loved Ripon and the life she and Dad had built there. Still, just getting through each day was becoming more and more difficult. Would she be able to cope with a new place where everything would be strange to her?

Our intentions were good. We knew God had given us a mission. What we had forgotten was that He wanted to help us with the details. How could we forget that important truth, when He had shown us so vividly that His hand was at work in every single aspect of our journey thus far?

God had shut the door to two retirement communities that would have been far too distant for us to see Mom and Dad regularly and participate in their care. He had prompted Nancy to go to the church at the exact time Sharon was going to meet with the pastor. The vice president of the company Peggy founded had recently taken on more responsibility, allowing Peggy the freedom to take time off for this move. Ann's last-minute flight was reasonably priced and available. The list went on and on.

> MARK 5:19 NIV
>
> *Jesus…said, "Go home to your family and tell them how much the LORD has done for you, and how He has had mercy on you."*

Hardly a day passed without clear evidence of God's active involvement in our situation, but by stumbling ahead of Him, we had caused our parents needless suffering. We were trying so hard to lessen their pain, but in this instance, we had done just the opposite.

Nancy tried to comfort Peggy: "But remember, she did say she loved him. She has been telling Dad she loves him ever since they met, not just in words, but in the way she hugged him when he came home from work each day, even in the way she fussed over his meals. She's just so afraid of making a move."

As we got up and turned off the lights, Ann said, "Let's just make sure we don't let this happen again. We know Who our Guide is. We have to continue to seek His will."

As the time for the move neared, Mom became more and more agitated, and we knew we had to find some relief for her and for us. The time had come to reach out to Dad's support team once again. Nancy and Dad headed over to see Bob, Dad's former business partner, and his wife, Sharon. She was the recently retired county nurse who had advised us that it was no longer safe for our parents to stay in the home they both loved.

Sharon greeted Nancy and Dad at the door. "We're glad you're here. We've been so worried about you and were wondering what we could do to help. Bob's in the sunroom. Let's go out and join him."

Nancy and Dad filled Bob and Sharon in on Mom's growing anxiety and her resistance to the move. She was not herself. She was angry, and the situation was becoming increasingly volatile.

Sharon asked what medications Mom was on, and Dad gave her the list. "You know, Al, you should call her doctor right away and get a prescription for anti-anxiety medication.

I'm surprised she's not on one already. There are several that have proven to be effective with Alzheimer's patients."

Nancy and Dad picked up the prescription on the way home, and we all felt confident that peace would be restored. That was not the case. Mom refused to take the medicine. Once again, we found ourselves in a cycle of reasoning, resistance, and forgetting. We had to find another approach to dealing with Mom's opposition. She needed the medication but wouldn't take it knowingly. Remembering a trick she had used to help us take our medicine when we were young, we decided to hide it in her food. It worked! Finally, Mom had some relief.

Even the proper medication didn't completely alleviate Mom's fears, and her resistance continued. We were still trying to force our reality on an Alzheimer's sufferer. The simple technique of distraction would have been a much better choice, but it wasn't until we realized how effective it could be that some measure of peace was restored to our family. Although this approach led to some disjointed conversations, distraction eliminated the fruitless explanations that were stressful for everybody.

Mom would ask, "Girls, now what is this about Virginia? Al, do you know what's going on?"

Before we learned to use distraction, we responded, "Mom, we're helping you move. We've talked about this every day."

PSALM 34:14b NLT

Work hard at living in peace with others.

Poor Mom; she'd get even more upset. We had a lot to learn. Once we discovered the benefits of distraction, our answers changed.

"Oh, Mom, I'm so glad you came down. I was just going outside to do some yard work, and I need you to show me where the leaf basket is."

Ann put her arm around Mom and led her outside. They were back in about ten minutes, the situation completely diffused. We had avoided another confrontation by distracting Mom from the source of her anxiety, and all of us were happier because of it.

Distraction was a technique that eventually became second nature to us. For example, one night, we were in the kitchen preparing dinner when Mom came in visibly upset.

"Girls, why are all those moving boxes in the living room? Al, do you know what's going on?"

Our response reflected our new understanding: "Oh, we'll take care of that later, Mom. Where are the napkins you want us to use? Are they on the porch? Let's eat out there tonight. I'll help you set the table."

We learned to take distraction a step further, by beginning with agreement. "Girls, I want to redecorate the living room. Let's go shopping today."

"Mom, that would be fun. Let's plan to do that tomorrow. Right now I want to show you the pictures I brought."

Mom was happy with our enthusiastic response and was

easily distracted by the pictures. The redecorating of the soon-to-be-vacated living room was quickly forgotten.

We could always support even the most impractical of Mom's ideas, suggesting that we do them later. She would be pleased that we agreed, then forget all about it as we involved her in an alternative activity. Many of these distractions didn't last long, but we became experts at coming up with new and inventive sources of distraction. God answered our prayers when our conversations with Mom became more relaxed and enjoyable once again.

Because we needed some time to get organized for the move, Peggy volunteered to take Mom out to the driving range. Mom and Dad hadn't played much in recent years but had always been avid golfers. Dad relished the fact that he had been able to play at least one round of golf with each of his three grandsons. The sport was a fun part of Mom and Dad's life together; in fact, they met on a golf course. We used to love hearing how Dad had spotted Mom on the next fairway and asked one of his buddies who she was. He had a date with her before they left the course, and the rest is—you know—history.

Peggy drove Mom out to the driving range near Green Lake. It was a beautiful day, and Mom was excited about their outing. They split a bucket of balls, and Peggy was thrilled to see how well Mom was doing and how much she enjoyed the activity. The range wasn't very crowded that day, so they took their time. They would hit a few, then sit on the bench for a while, sipping the sodas they'd gotten at the concession stand.

Getting through the whole bucket took a long time, but Peggy and Mom finally did it and started walking back to the stand to turn in their empty pail. A nice-looking man in his 30s approached them and spoke to Mom.

"Excuse me, ma'am. I just wanted to ask if you ever played golf professionally. You have a beautiful swing."

Mom's smile spoke volumes, and for the first time in a long time, she was not at a loss for words.

"Why, thank you. You have no idea how much that pleases me. No, I never played professionally, but I've played all my life. I haven't done much golfing recently. I have Alzheimer's disease, and I don't get out very much anymore."

He looked at her with incredible compassion and said, "Well, you should. You're a beautiful golfer."

To this day, you can't convince Peggy that she and Mom didn't meet an angel at the driving range.

As we spent more and more time with Mom and developed an appreciation for how Alzheimer's was affecting her, we were starting to echo Dad's words: "It's the disease. It's not your mom." Our frustration turned to compassion as we kept this insight in mind.

> JAMES 3:17 NLT
>
> *But the wisdom that comes from heaven is first of all pure. It is also peace loving, gentle at all times, and willing to yield to others. It is full of mercy and good deeds. It shows no partiality and is always sincere.*

We learned to choose topics of conversation that were of interest to Mom. We put away the moving boxes until Mom and Dad were on their way to Virginia and concentrated on loving our Mom. We were becoming the peacemakers God intended us to be.

Your Guide

The effects of Alzheimer's were becoming more pronounced in our mother, and keeping the peace was more and more challenging. We found that the combination of medication, distraction, and love was our most powerful tool. As we gained knowledge and experience in how to deal compassionately with Mom's resistance, the quality of life improved for all of us.

Nancy's daughter had told us that prescriptions were available that could have greatly reduced Mom's anxiety. We were unaware that none of these had been prescribed for her. Our entire family, and especially Mom, suffered needlessly.

Proper medication for the Alzheimer's sufferer can reduce resistance and alleviate stress for everyone involved in the situation. If your loved one is anxious or resistant, we encourage you to seek medical assistance as soon as possible. **Proper medication is crucial.**

One of our biggest failures was not recognizing soon enough the extent to which the disease was robbing Mom of her ability to reason. We repeated contentious discussions over and over again, finding it difficult to give up the logical approach. Distraction would have been infinitely more effective than trying to reason with her.

As hard as it is to abandon logic, we encourage you to give up the argument. Instead, distract your loved one and avoid confrontation whenever emotionally charged issues arise. Distraction becomes second nature as you gain more experience, and it is a great tool for keeping the peace.

> MATTHEW 5:9 NIV
>
> *"Blessed are the peacemakers,*
> *for they will be called sons of God."*

It's difficult to remain patient as your loved one becomes more resistant and you are worn down by lack of sleep and increasing responsibility. We hope that by being aware of some of the causes of resistance, you will experience less frustration and be able to call on your reserves of patience. In looking at our experience, we identified six possible reasons why a person with Alzheimer's would be resistant to reasonable suggestions. Following are examples of each:

- Confusion—When your loved one repeatedly responds to suggestions with "I just don't understand why we have to do this," remember that his or her life has become extremely confusing because of Alzheimer's.

- Fear—When your loved one refuses to participate in social situations, remember that interactions with others are becoming more challenging, and being home with family feels much safer.

- Paranoia—When your loved one refuses to consider having hired help in the home or hides "personal treasures," keep in mind that paranoia is a common symptom of Alzheimer's disease and imaginary threats are very real to the sufferer.

- Frustration—When you offer to help your loved one fix dinner or complete a project, and the response is a terse "I can do it myself," think about how irritated you would be if you could no longer accomplish tasks that were simple just a few months ago.

- Loss of control—When you take the car keys and refuse to allow your loved one to get behind the wheel, you can expect some pretty strong resistance. As you stand firm, be patient and understanding, remembering that this represents a significant loss of freedom for the person afflicted with Alzheimer's.

- Reduced social inhibition—When your formerly well-mannered loved one speaks inappropriately with strangers and refuses to respond to your redirection, tell yourself repeatedly, "It's the disease."

Alzheimer's sufferers may exhibit resistance in a number of different ways. Although we aren't experts in human behavior, we have become aware of the following types of opposition: *Confrontational* resistance seems to be common in people with Alzheimer's. It's the "Yes, you will"/"No, I won't" kind of interaction and can easily escalate into *emotional* resistance—crying, screaming, cursing, running away. Some sufferers resort to *physical* resistance. Others are *passive*, agreeing or remaining noncommittal while internally disagreeing and continuing their opposition in quiet noncompliance. Although it is difficult for those afflicted with Alzheimer's to pursue *legal* action, it is not uncommon for them to threaten caregivers with lawsuits. We are grateful that we have no experience with this form of resistance. If your loved one is able to obtain support for a legal action in opposition to your attempts to give care, be aware that the situation can be serious. You may want to secure your own counsel.

When faced with resistance in any form, take a deep breath and exhale a prayer. Ask God to help you speak the words that will maintain peace. If you reply quickly without thinking through your response, you may escalate the anger. Remember, as upsetting as resistance is to you, your loved one is in a fight for life itself.

> COLOSSIANS 3:12–15 NIV
>
> *Therefore, as God's chosen people, holy and dearly loved, clothe yourselves with compassion, kindness, humility, gentleness and patience. Bear with each other and forgive whatever grievances you may have against one another. Forgive as the Lord forgave you. And over all these virtues put on love, which binds them all together in perfect unity. Let the peace of Christ rule in your hearts, since as members of one body you were called to peace. And be thankful.*

Take a minute to evaluate your loved one's resistance. Do his or her concerns have merit, or is the problem one that doesn't even need to be addressed? Not all issues are significant; choose your battles or look for ways to compromise.

Ongoing resistance is especially stressful. Night after night, Mom would refuse to go out to dinner with Dad at the cozy family restaurant down the street from their church, but the need for Dad to ensure that they both ate nutritious meals was becoming more serious. Dad could not give in to her wishes on this point. Instead, he tended to ignore her protests, help her with her coat, and gently escort her out the door.

Because Alzheimer's attacks the ability to think clearly, we recommend that you avoid sharing potentially upsetting information with your loved one. This suggestion may be especially difficult to put into practice if you have shared everything with each other in the past. Keep in mind, however, that your loved one is changing and the extent of your openness must change as well. Before speaking, ask yourself: Will sharing this information benefit my loved one, or would I be better off keeping it to myself?

At the same time that you are becoming more careful about what you say, your loved one is losing the ability to think rationally. Alzheimer's sufferers commonly make totally unrealistic claims: "You go out to eat by yourself. I can fix a seven-course dinner for myself," or "I'm an excellent driver, and you can't stop me from driving," or "If you move, the neighbors will take care of me." These conversations are almost always frustrating and frequently hurtful. They will test your patience and your faith. Remember, "It's the disease"; remind yourself, "I can do everything through Him Who gives me strength."

As with everything you do in caring for your loved one, once you make a decision, don't beat yourself up about how you handled resistance. Caring for an Alzheimer's sufferer is undoubtedly a role you would not have chosen and for which you probably have not been trained. When you do make a mistake, ask the Lord for forgiveness and forgive yourself. Then, forget it. God will. Just do the best you can and stay close to Him in prayer.

A Prayer

Heavenly Father, You are the source of perfect peace, and You have called us to be Your peacemakers in this world. Take away our unkind thoughts. Hold our tongues and help us to pray for Your guidance before we react to resistance. Give us words of healing and love rather than divisiveness and anger. Thy will be done. In Jesus' name, Amen.

The Fruit of the Spirit from God's Word

GALATIANS 5:22–23a NIV

*But the fruit of the Spirit is love, joy, peace,
patience, kindness, goodness, faithfulness, gentleness
and self-control.*

Additional Scriptures

PSALM 29:11 NIV

> *The LORD gives strength to His people;*
> *the LORD blesses His people with peace.*

PROVERBS 19:11 NIV

> *A man's wisdom gives him patience;*
> *it is to his glory to overlook an offense.*

ISAIAH 26:3 NLT

> *You will keep in perfect peace all who trust in You,*
> *whose thoughts are fixed on You!*

JEREMIAH 10:23 NIV

> *I know, O LORD, that a man's life is not his own;*
> *it is not for man to direct his steps.*

LUKE 21:14–15 NIV

> *"But make up your mind not to worry beforehand how you*
> *will defend yourselves. For I will give you words and wisdom*
> *that none of your adversaries will be able to resist or*
> *contradict."*

ROMANS 14:19 NASB

> *So then we pursue the things which make for peace and the*
> *building up of one another.*

1 PETER 3:9 NIV

> *Do not repay evil with evil or insult with insult, but with*
> *blessing, because to this you were called so that you may inherit*
> *a blessing.*

Chapter 7: When a Move Is Best

How do we get there from here?

Our Story

"Where's Mom? It's time to leave for church."

The congregation of St. Peter's Episcopal Church was a close-knit community of believers, many of whom had known Mom and Dad since they had joined the church when they moved to Ripon. Dad was a church leader, and Mom had been active in the ladies' group until her illness made that service impossible for her.

Dad's father had been a Methodist minister, and our family attended services at the Methodist church in Watertown, Wisconsin, where Mom and Dad began their married life. The day we moved to Ripon, the ladies of St. Peter's walked down the hill from the church to bring us our first dinner in our new home. We had found a new church family, a comfortable one for Mom, who had been raised in the Episcopalian church, and a tradition Dad grew to love.

The church ladies' custom of preparing food for special family occasions continued today as we met in the church hall for a farewell coffee hour to honor our parents following Sunday services. Saying goodbye to the church was an emotional experience for all of us. We had gathered here for family weddings, baptisms, and funerals—the monumental passages in ordinary lives, lives made extraordinary by the support of the church family and the presence of God.

ACTS 20:28 NIV

"Keep watch over yourselves and all the flock of which the Holy Spirit has made you overseers. Be shepherds of the church of God, which He bought with His own blood."

We entered the big red doors, and the wooden floors creaked beneath our feet as we moved down the central aisle; sunlight filtered through the beautiful stained-glass windows. It was easy to feel God's presence. We made our way to the family pew and knelt on the kneeling pads that Mom had lovingly needle-pointed just a few years before.

PSALM 27:4 NIV

One thing I ask of the LORD,
  this is what I seek:
that I may dwell in the house of the LORD
  all the days of my life,
to gaze upon the beauty of the LORD
and to seek Him in His temple.

Surrounded by the intricately carved dark walls and the beautiful statues of the saints, we looked up at the large wooden cross that dominated the intimate chapel. We prayed that Christ would similarly dominate our lives, to lighten the burden of the move, just as He had removed the weight of our sins.

The serenity of the church and its grounds and the warmth of the fellowship inside were in sharp contrast to our mother's emotional state. At the coffee hour, Mom was faced with questions about their new home and comments about how much they would be missed. She became increasingly upset. She was caught up in a situation in which she wanted no part, and she needed to get out of there.

Sensing Mom's agitation, we began to say our goodbyes. Suddenly, Ann's voice broke through the cheerful chatter: "Where's Mom?" We immediately started looking. Nancy and Peggy searched the lower level while Ann and her husband headed upstairs.

"Bill, will you look in the sanctuary? I'll check outside."

Ann rushed out the back door into the beautiful gardens. As she scanned the area, she caught a glimpse of periwinkle blue out of the corner of her eye. She raced down the garden path that led to the millpond. Her steps slowed as she heard a young voice call out, "Ruth, is that you?"

Mom was standing on the bank of the pond, looking across its surface. Ann hesitated, not wanting to startle her and curious about the young fisherman who had called out across the water. He and Mom obviously knew each other because he had called Mom by name.

"Yes, it is," Mom answered. "How's the fishing?"

"I put my line in just before you came down. Is that your church?"

"Yes, and I love it so much, but I guess I'm going away for a while. Could you keep an eye on our yard while I'm gone?"

"Sure. Are you going on a vacation?"

"I don't know."

Ann walked up to Mom, put her arm around her, and slowly led her back up the path to the church.

"Who's your nice young friend, Mom?"

"Oh, he's a neighbor. He likes to come over and pick up crabapples from under our tree. I can't remember why he wants them, but we always have a nice visit. He calls me Ruth. I kind of like that."

PROVERBS 14:31b NIV

...whoever is kind to the needy honors God.

"He seems to really like you. I'm glad you got to see him today," Ann said, giving Mom a little hug.

Nancy and Peggy came hurrying out of the church and were relieved to see Mom and Ann coming up the garden path.

"There you are. We've been looking everywhere for you," Peggy called out. She sent up a silent prayer of thanks.

"Mom, you always look so beautiful in that periwinkle blue dress," Nancy added.

Dad and Bill met us in the churchyard. Dad took Mom's hand and we followed them down the hill as we left the church and the millpond behind.

"Girls, I'm heading down to the drug store. Your mom's out on the back porch. Be sure you keep an eye on her while I'm gone."

Monday was moving day. The three of us took a moment to stand together and watch Dad drive his car down Tygert Street for the last time. Our Dad was a pharmacist and was going to say goodbye to the store he and his partner, Bob, had built. It was his place. He was leaving the staff he had mentored. They were more than business associates; they were good friends. As Dad had become increasingly isolated by Mom's disease, the store and its employees were his link to the outside world.

When Dad returned, he hung his keys on the hook for the last time. We were grateful that he had decided to leave the car behind and give up driving because his sight was starting to fail. He went out to sit on his bench in the garden. He surely was thanking God for the many wonderful years he and Mom had shared in this friendly community and praying for strength for the days ahead. Dad was saddened by the prospect of leaving the home he loved, but he knew God's hand was at work in this move, and he looked forward in faith.

PSALM 18:32 NIV

It is God who arms me with strength and makes my way perfect.

Although Dad fully understood the implications of the move, Mom did not. The Ruth who would live in Virginia was not the same Ruth who had enjoyed a full life in Ripon. Unfortunately, that active, outgoing woman would be left behind.

Most of Mom's adult identity was wrapped up in Ripon—wife of a respected businessman; mother of three daughters; active church member; head of the committee to build a new library; supporter of the local college; local United Way board member; women's club officer; member of the historical society, study club, and bridge club; volunteer supporter of many local charities and community events.

Before Mom's illness, she had a full social life. The phone was always ringing. She and Dad golfed together and with friends. They entertained and were entertained in return. They were founding members of a Ripon couples club. In Wisconsin, Mom was well known, well respected, and well loved. At her new home in Virginia, none of the people would know her in the same way.

> PROVERBS 11:16a NIV
>
> *A kindhearted woman gains respect...*

Did Mom have a sense of the loss? Is that why she was so resistant to the move? We would never really know.

Although Mom never completely gave up the fight to stay in Wisconsin, we discovered that her heart was no longer in it. The night before we left, she made it clear to us that her heart would be traveling to Virginia with Dad.

After an early dinner, we went upstairs to help Mom and Dad pack their suitcases. They would live out of them for a week in the guest cottage before we completed moving them into their own home. We had been praying about this moment for days. How would we convince Mom to pack for a move she still refused to make?

We decided to pack for a "trip" instead of a move. In Mom's presence, we dealt with the subject as if she and Dad would be going to Virginia for a visit, something they had done many times in the past.

"Let's pack your summer clothes, Mom. It's pretty warm in Virginia right now. Which nighties would you like to take?" Ann was talking quickly and enthusiastically, hoping to get Mom caught up in the project.

Mom's answer was a delightful surprise: "Well, if I were going on a trip, I guess I'd want to take these." We spent the next hour in a series of "If you were's," and Mom was packed.

We had made plans to have lunch with the pastor and leave for the airport from the restaurant to eliminate the possibility of Mom's becoming upset when we left the house. Maintaining the pretense of merely leaving to go out for lunch would be easier than facing the finality of closing the door forever.

The pastor sat across from Dad and spoke, "Al, it has come to me that there's a mission for you in Virginia. This will be an opportunity for you to reach out to your grandchildren and for

> PSALM 71:18 NIV
>
> *Even when I am old and gray,*
>   *do not forsake me, O God,*
>
> *till I declare Your power to the next*
>   *generation,*
> *Your might to all who are to come.*

them to get to know you. It's important, Al, because grandparents have a unique role to play in the lives of their grandchildren."

We had planned every aspect of the move in detail. Ann and Bill flew with Mom and Dad to Virginia while Nancy and Peggy stayed behind to pack and move their household belongings.

The drive to the airport and the flight to Virginia went off without a hitch. Mom seemed to enjoy the adventure, and Dad was relieved to be on the way. Peggy's husband, Hal, met the flight, and with baggage collected, the travelers were en route to our parents' new home. Ultimately, Mom had said yes to the pastor's question. She did love Dad enough to go with him wherever he went.

Meanwhile in Wisconsin, Nancy's eldest daughter had arrived to help Nancy and Peggy pack and move. Earlier in the week, friends had taken the folks for a day at the cottage, giving us an opportunity to do some detailed planning. Armed with a floor plan showing the measurements of Mom and Dad's new home, we had identified all the furniture that would go with them. Dad was happy to give away everything they didn't need. He hoped it would be used and appreciated by other members of the family.

The physical move took about a week, and it was at least a month before we felt that Mom and Dad were at home in their new surroundings. God had more than answered our prayers by leading us to a home that was, in many ways, a miniature of the house they'd left behind—another colonial, gray with green shutters.

Nancy's youngest daughter had organized the welcome to Virginia. The great grandchildren's homemade welcome sign hanging from the pillars brought tears to Dad's eyes as he and Mom stood hand in hand. He recalled the pastor's words: "…there's a mission for you in Virginia…grandparents have a unique role to play in the lives of their grandchildren." They were already waiting for him, and he was excited.

> PSALM 89:1 NIV
>
> *I will sing of the LORD's great love forever;*
> *with my mouth I will make Your faithfulness*
> *known through all generations.*

Your Guide

Our situation demanded that our parents relocate to a retirement community, but not every family facing Alzheimer's has to make that decision. For many, moving in with other family members is the best option, although such a move must be made with a thorough understanding of the needs and demands of people with Alzheimer's disease. Make sure you're not just trading one unsafe situation for another. Consider who will be providing the care. Do potential caregivers have the physical strength, time, resources, and know-how to do the job without endangering their own health and safety as well as that of the Alzheimer's sufferer?

We believe that in most cases, a move is required for safety at some point in the progression of the disease. Because a move to a retirement community with a continuum of care was necessary in our case, that is the situation we discuss here.

Most families should at least consider the possibility of moving as soon as a loved one exhibits signs of dementia. Relocating can allow you to be closer to family, give you increased access to needed care, and make your life more manageable.

With rare exception, the sooner a move is made, the better. Adapting to a new environment is easier for the Alzheimer's sufferer when he or she still has some short-term memory. Further, an early move that lessens the burden for the primary caregiver has the potential to add years to his or her life.

The following paragraphs offer tips to help a move go smoothly. In general, our advice is to:

- Distract the Alzheimer's sufferer from moving plans and preparations, if necessary.

- Resolve as many details before the move as possible, including making a floor plan of the new home and arranging your furniture on paper.

- Give valuable or sentimental items you no longer need to family members who can use and enjoy them.

- Arrange to store, sell, donate, or discard unwanted possessions.

- Inform friends and neighbors about the move and make plans to stay in touch; keep goodbyes brief and upbeat.

- Begin to assemble a support team in your new location and become a member of the community there.

Of course, moving requires attention to a great number of details. Make sure you have an adequate supply of prescriptions to get you through the transition period. Get copies of medical and dental records, as well as necessary legal and financial papers. If you are moving out of state, it is advisable to have an attorney in your new home state review legal documents to ensure that they conform to state law. Inform anyone with whom you wish to maintain regular contact of your new address. Pay particular attention to any companies, agencies, or organizations from which you receive income, such as investment companies, the Social Security Administration, insurance companies, and so on. Check your local post office, moving company, or real estate agent for information packets containing recommendations for changing your address.

> COLOSSIANS 3:23 NIV
>
> *Whatever you do, work at it with all your heart, as working for the Lord, not for men...*

Detailed planning up front will make the physical move go much more smoothly. Again, look for information packets from a moving company or real estate agent to assist you in this process. Reserve the dates you need with a moving company or truck rental office and helpers as soon as you know your schedule. If you have friends who have moved recently and have been seeking a way to help, this is their opportunity. They may assist in packing and will probably be able to make your move easier in other ways because of their experience.

In all likelihood, your move will be to a smaller home, so take less rather than more. Early on, we obtained a floor plan of Mom and Dad's new home. We visited the retirement community and, armed with a tape measure, wrote down all the dimensions—the length of each wall, the height of every window, the locations of doors, the positions of electrical outlets, television and telephone connections, and so on. We noted every measurement that would help in the placement of furniture.

Creating a detailed floor plan before you load even one piece of furniture on the truck can save you a good deal of work and, possibly, expense. A floor plan will enable you to determine what size moving truck you need. You will also avoid taking furniture that won't fit in your new home or leaving behind necessary items that will fit. The plan will allow you to arrange your furniture beforehand, on paper, to assist with placement when you arrive at the site.

Using the floor plan, you can also determine the disposition of your belongings. Items may be:

- Moved to your new home
- Given to family members or friends
- Sold
- Donated to charitable organizations
- Discarded

HEBREWS 13:16 NIV

And do not forget to do good and to share with others, for with such sacrifices God is pleased.

If time runs out or you choose not to part with belongings that don't fit comfortably into your new home, storage units may be a temporary solution to relieve crowding. We were somewhat grateful that our parents' home was not sold for several months. The extra time allowed us to get them settled in their new home and determine what else they needed before we distributed their remaining possessions. If you're moving from a home you own and it is not possible to postpone the sale, you might lease a storage unit or ask your real estate agent about a rent-back situation.

Leaving the comfort and familiarity of the known is difficult. We provided Mom and Dad with photos and brochures of their new home to ease this process. Keep the focus on the future rather than the past.

At the same time, staying in contact with friends and neighbors who are left behind is also important. We composed and sent out a letter informing people of our parents' move. The letter described their new home, included the address and phone number, and encouraged people to call, write, or visit. We knew that the support of old friends would help our parents as they made new ones. Dad also kept up their subscription to *The Ripon Commonwealth-Press* and looked forward to its arrival every week.

We left much of Dad's support team in Wisconsin when we accompanied our parents to Virginia. We would eventually enlist others in the effort, but during this settling-in time, it was essential that we three daughters and our husbands assume the responsibility for their transition.

At least one of us stayed with Mom and Dad every night for the first two and a half weeks. During the day, we unpacked, hung pictures and curtains, and went shopping for groceries and necessary household items. We dealt with installers who came to hook up the services we had arranged in advance—electricity, phone, Internet, and cable television. As time went on, we located, scheduled visits with, and transported Mom and Dad to doctors, dentists, hearing specialists, and other medical-care providers. We visited several churches and continued to attend with them regularly after they selected a new church home.

The new community offered many amenities with which Mom and Dad needed to become familiar. Having meals with them in the new environment was a pleasure for us; we also got to know the drivers of the van, the people at the front desk, and the staff in the deli. We took Mom to the beauty parlor and Dad to get haircuts. As we helped our parents through this period of adjustment, we began to feel as if we, too, were part of the community. Both staff and residents were incredibly welcoming, and Mom and Dad made new friends quickly.

Once we returned to our former routines, we continued to have frequent contact with Mom and Dad. Maintaining that connection was important to them, and it was important to us. The promises we had made to Dad back in Wisconsin were being realized. He and Mom were safe and had regular visits from family. They hadn't just left their old life; they had moved on to a new one.

A Prayer

Heavenly Father, only You are omnipresent, with us always wherever we are. What a comfort that is to us. Thank You for guiding our steps, whether we are on a journey to a new home or staying in familiar places. Help us to focus on what lies ahead with eager anticipation, secure in the knowledge that You equip us with all we need to do Your will. Thy will be done. In Jesus' name, Amen.

Hope from God's Word

PSALM 107:30 NIV

They were glad when it grew calm,
and He guided them to their desired haven.

Additional Scriptures

JOSHUA 1:9 NIV

> *"...Be strong and courageous. Do not be terrified; do not be discouraged, for the LORD your God will be with you wherever you go."*

PSALM 16:6 NIV

> *The boundary lines have fallen for me in pleasant places;*
> *surely I have a delightful inheritance.*

PSALM 91:11 NLT

> *For He orders His angels*
> *to protect you wherever you go.*

PSALM 119:105 NIV

> *Your Word is a lamp to my feet*
> *and a light for my path.*

PSALM 139:9–10 NIV

> *If I rise on the wings of the dawn,*
> *if I settle on the far side of the sea,*
> *even there Your hand will guide me,*
> *Your right hand will hold me fast.*

JOHN 14:23 NIV

> *Jesus replied, "If anyone loves Me, he will obey My teaching. My Father will love him, and We will come to him and make Our home with him."*

ACTS 17:28a NIV

> *"'For in Him we live and move and have our being.'..."*

Chapter 8: Signs of Advancing Alzheimer's

How can I cope with this new reality?

Our Story

> *"Hi, girls. Your mother just headed 'upstairs' to bed. We're looking forward to seeing you tomorrow."*

Dad enjoyed the humor in Mom's continuing to say that she was going upstairs to bed even though they were now living in a one-story home. His health was beginning to improve in this new environment. They were receiving nourishing meals; they didn't have to worry about yard work or housework; he was attending exercise classes when he could find someone to stay with Mom; and they were no longer isolated. Many of their new friends were dealing with similar problems of aging.

The three of us arrived the next day in time to help Mom get ready for dinner. We found her on the phone talking with her sister-in-law. Mom and Aunt Dorie had become especially

> 1 CORINTHIANS 13:13 NLT
>
> *There are three things that will endure—faith, hope, and love—and the greatest of these is love.*

close during our uncle's battle with Alzheimer's. Dorie had been very thoughtful after the folks' move, writing and calling them frequently.

As we overheard Mom's side of the conversation, we were grateful that she felt comfortable discussing the effects of Alzheimer's with Dorie, but it broke our hearts to hear her say, "Dorie, I really can't do anything anymore." We hadn't realized that Mom was aware of the toll the disease was taking on her ability to function normally.

Although she tried to get dressed by herself and we had organized her closet to make the task as easy as possible, she was no longer able to select appropriate clothing. When she got off the phone, we went back to the bedroom to help her dress for dinner.

Knowing how anxious Mom was when faced with going to the main dining room for dinner, we kept the mood light. Nancy's husband, Richard, provided the perfect topic of conversation.

Nancy said to Mom, "I heard you and Richard had a date for ice cream this afternoon. Did he really take you along to the hardware store, too?"

Mom was delighted to be reminded of her outing with Richard. She loved riding in his red sports car, and Richard made sure she had fun when she was with him. Their outings were a safe and joyful escape from the chaos that was beginning to overwhelm Mom's life.

What was particularly unusual about Mom's adventures with Richard was that riding in vehicles had always made her nervous. One of the small blessings of Alzheimer's was that as her focus narrowed, many things that had once been anxiety-provoking were no longer frightening.

Our lively discussion about her afternoon activities had distracted Mom during the potentially stressful process of getting dressed for dinner. We finished and went to join Dad.

As we entered the living room, Mom said she wanted to introduce us to her next-door neighbor. We thought she was heading for the door, but she stopped in front of a large mirror on the living room wall and waved at her reflection. "Girls, say hi to my friend. She's so nice, but she doesn't say much. I wish she'd come over and visit."

As much as we'd become accustomed to Mom's frequently strange behavior, it took us a moment to respond. Ann was the first to recover, "It's so good to meet you. We're glad our mom has such a nice friend." We were shocked...the first person Mom couldn't recognize was herself.

> 1 CORINTHIANS 13:12 NLT
>
> *Now we see things imperfectly as in a poor mirror, but then we will see everything with perfect clarity. All that I know now is partial and incomplete, but then I will know everything completely, just as God knows me now.*

The community van arrived in the cul-de-sac, and the driver beeped the horn, calling the neighborhood to dinner. Once again, Mom told Dad that she wanted to stay home. Dad knew that she was trying to avoid social situations, but he also knew that they had to be careful not to slip back into isolation, as they had in their old home. She hesitated, but Dad lovingly insisted.

"Oh, Ruth, you look so nice. Let's go have dinner with our girls."

> DEUTERONOMY 31:6 NASB
>
> *"Be strong and courageous, do not be afraid or tremble at them, for the LORD your God is the One Who goes with you. He will not fail you or forsake you."*

Dad opened the door. Mom took a deep breath and led the way to the van, her shoulders squared, marching almost like a soldier. She was steeling herself for the challenge that lay ahead.

The van driver hopped out and offered his hand to Mom, "Hello, Mrs. Nimz, let me help you aboard. I see you've brought your daughters with you." Mom relaxed in the warm greeting, and we headed for the main building.

As we entered the dining room, we were pleased to see how many people already greeted Mom and Dad by name. "Tonight we'll just sit with family," Dad said. "Usually I make sure we share a table with at least one other couple. We've gotten to know a lot of the residents that way."

The friendly hostess, noticing Dad's hearing aids, seated us in a quiet corner where Dad could participate more fully in the conversation. The dining room was attractive and comfortable, and we knew from past dinners that although the menu was limited, the food would be delicious. Dad asked Mom just a couple of questions, then took over all the details of ordering for her.

After an enjoyable dinner, we piled back in the van and were dropped off at our parents' cozy home. As we sat in the living room, Mom's attention was drawn outside. "There they are again, Al. Why do they keep having parties in our back-yard?"

Peggy immediately went over to the window to see what Mom was talking about. The only thing visible was a lawn tractor left behind at the end of the day. Closing the blinds, Peg reassured Mom, "I think they're finished for today. I'm sure they won't be bothering you anymore tonight."

Dad drew Mom's attention to the small bottle he held in his hand, "Luv, here are my eye drops. Would you please put them in before you go 'up' to bed?"

Even though Dad was perfectly capable of putting in his own eye drops, he was sensitive to Mom's desire to be his help-mate. We were happy to see that she was still able to do this one small thing for Dad. Mom finished her task, gave Dad a good-night kiss, and headed "upstairs."

> GENESIS 2:18 NIV
>
> *The LORD God said, "It is not good for the man to be alone. I will make a helper suitable for him."*

Your Guide

Learning to accept and deal effectively with the sometimes bizarre behaviors caused by Alzheimer's has similarities to learning to cope with a physical disability. The sooner you make the adjustment, the easier and more peaceful your lives will be. Let go, lighten up, laugh a lot, and look at life through your loved one's new lenses.

> PSALM 73:26 NLT
>
> *My health may fail, and my spirit may grow weak, but God remains the strength of my heart; He is mine forever.*

The abilities of a person with Alzheimer's to maintain focus, comprehend ideas, and reason diminish over time. Consequently, watching television and reading may no longer be of interest to your loved one. These mental pastimes can be replaced by simpler, more tactile activities, such as:

- Folding and refolding baskets of towels

- Working in the garden

- Arranging flowers

- Coloring and finger painting

- Working with modeling clay

- Making collages with magazine pictures

Purses were a source of enjoyment for Mom as she sorted through the many items they held. A man might similarly enjoy going through a toolbox or a briefcase filled with a number of small, safe objects.

Losing touch with reality becomes more of an issue as the disease advances. Although Mom's vision and hearing were, and remain to this day, nearly perfect, she began to misidentify objects, suggesting nonsensical substitutions for common, everyday items. At one time, she enjoyed looking at traffic lights, commenting on the pretty Christmas decorations. She was once convinced that a tree limb was actually a German shepherd. These were generally harmless misinterpretations, and we learned that trying to convince her that she was mistaken was futile and upsetting. Put your distraction skills to work, and save everyone a lot of frustration.

For weeks at a time, Mom's speech has become nothing but gibberish—completely unintelligible. We continue to talk with her as if her conversation makes sense. So far, after a period of time, her small dialogue of stock phrases returns, and we are blessed by the ability to communicate with her again, even in such a limited way.

Short-term memory loss has become much more apparent. If we leave the room, Mom forgets we have been with her at all. At times, this is an advantage. Instead of making her sad by having to say goodbye, we merely step out of her narrowed range of focus, and she forgets we were ever there.

We purposely eliminate from our conversation such phrases as "you remember...," "we just talked about...," and "don't you know...." A well-meaning but untrained caregiver would frequently ask Mom who we were when we came to visit. Her

> JOHN 10:14 NIV
>
> *"I am the Good Shepherd; I know My sheep and My sheep know Me..."*

inability to recall our names was frustrating for Mom and painful for us. For Mom, even the immediate past is gone, and trying to force her to remember serves no useful purpose. You can't force a blind person to see, and you can't force an Alzheimer's patient to remember.

You can expect a gradual decline in the ability to perform common life skills, such as bathing and dressing. Because these functions are second nature to all of us, as a caregiver, you may be unaware that such tasks involve too many steps for the patient to handle. A little preparation and cueing can postpone the inevitable loss of these skills. For example, you might:

- Suggest a shower or bath.

- Put out towels.

- Lay out fresh clothes in a helpful order.

As the disease progresses, the sufferer may no longer recognize himself or herself in a mirror. The loss of self-recognition can be more than a little unsettling, even frightening, to the person with Alzheimer's. If reflections are disturbing to your loved one, replace mirrors with photos. A covering attached with Velcro for the bathroom mirror will allow the caregiver access to the mirror as needed without exposing the patient to the fear that a stranger is in the room.

One of the most difficult times for us to deal with was a period when our mother tried to feed real food to dolls and stuffed animals. She had lost the ability to distinguish between what was real and what was imaginary. We learned to prepare visitors ahead of time for this potentially awkward situation. Even the youngest were able to understand that Great Grandma was sick. We set aside our own discomfort and allowed Mom to enjoy the simple pleasures of her fantasy world.

You may find that your loved one goes through a stage of paranoia. Hiding things and imagining that people are talking or laughing about them are typical symptoms of those with advancing Alzheimer's. It was a blessing for all of us when Mom moved out of this stage and was no longer obsessed by unreasonable fears.

> EPHESIANS 4:2 NIV
>
> *Be completely humble and gentle; be patient, bearing with one another in love.*

Some people afflicted with Alzheimer's disease experience delusions and/or hallucinations. These symptoms can be caused by a variety of factors, some totally unrelated to Alzheimer's. If this is a problem for your loved one, see a doctor to determine the cause and obtain appropriate treatment.

It's not uncommon to encounter Alzheimer's sufferers whose confusion and frustration can be expressed only by yelling, screaming, cursing, hitting, kicking, or throwing things—rather like a child having a tantrum. If you observe your loved one exhibiting these kinds of behaviors, first make sure that everyone is safe and you have adequate help to handle the situation. (Call 911 if necessary.) Then, try one or more of the following:

- Distraction
- Soothing touch
- Patient medication

If this behavior is ongoing or severe enough for you to be concerned about the safety of the patient or others—even once—you need to take action. The solution may be as simple as having the physician adjust the patient's medication. You might hire in-home help. Moving your loved one into a specialized care facility may become your only option.

> 1 CORINTHIANS 16:13–14 NIV
>
> *Be on your guard; stand firm in the faith; be men of courage; be strong. Do everything in love.*

People with Alzheimer's seem to lose the ability to take in everything that's going on around them. If two of us would stand next to Mom, one on either side, she could focus on only one of us. The other seemed to disappear from view. When you observe this symptom, we recommend that you interact with your loved one individually, getting right in front, at eye level.

The loss of other sensory abilities can be replaced by touch. Our mother loves a good hand or foot rub with a perfumed lotion, and she enjoys as many hugs and kisses as we can give her. Just holding her hand helps her maintain awareness that we are with her.

Inevitably, the time will come when your loved one no

longer recognizes you. This situation is one of the toughest you'll encounter. Although Mom no longer knows our names or our relationship to her, she is always happy to see us, and we sense an occasional spark of recognition. We have learned to be satisfied with this small but special connection.

Alzheimer's sufferers have no past and no future. They live in the present moment. Learn to enjoy and appreciate those moments.

> PROVERBS 3:27 NIV
>
> *Do not withhold good from those who deserve it, when it is in your power to act.*

A Prayer

Heavenly Father, You are the strength of our hearts. Your love is always with us. Thank You for giving us hearts that seek to understand and help each other—hearts that recognize You as Lord. Help us to persevere, responding to difficult situations with love. Thy will be done. In Jesus' name, Amen.

Compassion from God's Word

LAMENTATIONS 3:21–23 NIV

*Yet this I call to mind
and therefore I have hope:
Because of the LORD's great love we are not consumed,
for His compassions never fail.
They are new every morning;
great is Your faithfulness.*

Additional Scriptures

PSALM 31:9–10, 14–16 NIV

> *Be merciful to me, O LORD, for I am in distress;*
> *my eyes grow weak with sorrow,*
> *my soul and my body with grief.*
> *My life is consumed by anguish*
> *and my years by groaning;*
> *my strength fails because of my affliction,*
> *and my bones grow weak.*
>
> *But I trust in You, O LORD;*
> *I say, "You are my God."*
> *My times are in Your hands;*
> *deliver me from my enemies*
> *and from those who pursue me.*
> *Let Your face shine on Your servant;*
> *save me in Your unfailing love.*

PSALM 73:28 NLT

> *But as for me, how good it is to be near God!*
> *I have made the Sovereign LORD my shelter,*
> *and I will tell everyone about the wonderful things*
> *You do.*

PSALM 119:147 NIV

> *I rise before dawn and cry for help;*
> *I have put my hope in Your Word.*

MATTHEW 11:28 NIV

> *"Come to Me, all you who are weary and burdened, and*
> *I will give you rest."*

JOHN 16:33 NIV

"I have told you these things, so that in Me you may have peace. In this world you will have trouble. But take heart! I have overcome the world."

2 CORINTHIANS 4:7–9 NIV

But we have this treasure in jars of clay to show that this all-surpassing power is from God and not from us. We are hard pressed on every side, but not crushed; perplexed, but not in despair; persecuted, but not abandoned; struck down, but not destroyed.

JAMES 1:2–4 NIV

Consider it pure joy, my brothers, whenever you face trials of many kinds, because you know that the testing of your faith develops perseverance. Perseverance must finish its work so that you may be mature and complete, not lacking anything.

Chapter 9: When Home Care Is No Longer an Option

How can I contribute to quality care?

Our Story

> *"Girls, we can't find your mother. Can you come?"*

Dad was taking a lot of naps during the day to make up for the sleep he lost because of Mom's wakefulness at night. During these naptimes, Mom sometimes slipped outside, but Dad always found her nearby when he awoke. Today, however, there was panic in Dad's voice when he told us he couldn't find Mom. Although security was on the way, we knew we needed to get to their home as soon as possible.

We were thankful that Ann was visiting and the three of us were able to go together. As we drove to the retirement community, we thought about the nearby pond and woods that had seemed so attractive when we chose their new home. Had they become a threat to Mom's safety? Where was she?

By the time we arrived, Mom and Dad were at home, and Mom was resting in the bedroom. "Dad, what happened?"

Dad sat down in his easy chair and drew a deep breath. He looked older and more frail than he had just a few days before. "Your mother and I walked over to the main building for her appointment with the visiting podiatrist. When the doctor came into the examining room, Ruth panicked. I don't know what frightened her. All of a sudden, she started screaming and ran out of the room. I couldn't keep up with her."

"Where did she go? How did you find her? Is she okay?"

"She's just fine, but the doctor gave her something so she would sleep. Evidently, when she left the clinic, she made it across the street but didn't know how to get home. She ran into our neighbors' house and bolted right out the back door toward the pond. The neighbors know that Ruth has Alzheimer's. They caught up with her, took her back inside, and calmed her down. I had no sooner called you girls than they showed up at the front door."

> EZEKIEL 34:11–12 NIV
>
> *"For this is what the Sovereign LORD says: I Myself will search for My sheep and look after them. As a shepherd looks after his scattered flock when he is with them, so will I look after My sheep...."*

"Dad, how horrible for both of you. We're so glad you called. Are you okay?"

Dad could only shake his head in response to Ann's question. Words failed us all. Peggy reached for Dad's hand and said, "Dad, let's pray. The Lord knows we're suffering, that our whole family is in pain. He promises never to forsake us or to leave us. He'll help us get through this."

Peggy was only repeating what she'd heard many times before from Dad. In the past, he'd been the one to remind us of the source of our comfort.

As we sat in our parents' living room and Mom slept in the bedroom, we were all aware of the space that was growing between our mother's life and ours. We asked the Lord to fill the emptiness. We prayed and wept, then sat silently, waiting for the Holy Spirit to give us the strength to go on. He did not fail us; we felt His presence, and eventually, we began to speak again. We didn't have a lot to say, but we knew we were facing a decision that should be made at this time and place.

"Let's not go over to the dining room tonight. Let's just eat here," Ann suggested.

We all agreed and were soon seated at the table with bowls of hot soup and warm bread in front of us. Nancy turned to Dad: "I'll lead the blessing tonight, Dad." We joined hands and thanked God for His provision and asked for His blessing. We prayed that He would be with Mom and Dad in the days to come and that He would lead us in His will.

As we slowly ate our simple meal, we talked about what the day's crisis meant for the future. Perhaps we already knew, but we had to express our thoughts to clarify the decision to come.

"Has this ever happened before?" Ann finally asked.

"It's been happening more and more. She's so scared and

confused. I thought I could keep my eye on her, but I just can't do it every minute of every day."

Dad's voice trailed off and we were all silent. There were many tears, and then the words were spoken.

"We know you want to keep Mom here with you, but it's just not safe anymore." Dad slowly nodded his head in agreement. Our hearts were breaking for our parents. They had spent only six months together in their new home. We had all hoped it would be much longer.

> PSALM 25:16–17 NIV
>
> *Turn to me and be gracious to me,*
> *for I am lonely and afflicted.*
> *The troubles of my heart have*
> *multiplied;*
> *free me from my anguish.*

When we talked with the staff in the Alzheimer's unit, they suggested that Dad bring Mom over for a visit the next day. He agreed to have her spend an hour or two as the initial step in an eventual move several days later. While she participated in activities there, we went upstairs to the administrative office and helped Dad fill out paperwork for Mom's move from independent living to the safety of the Alzheimer's unit.

Dad was obviously struggling. We saw tears in his eyes as he mechanically took out his wallet and retrieved the required information. He was clearly not ready for this separation. The only time he and Mom had been apart for more than a night or two since their wedding was when Dad served in the Navy during World War II.

The paperwork was interrupted by a phone call from the Alzheimer's unit. Mom's visit wasn't going as planned; she was extremely agitated. We were asked to have Mom move to the unit immediately to avoid putting her through this trauma twice. We had come to the most difficult part of our Alzheimer's journey, and we could do little to ease the pain our parents were experiencing. Mom would not be going home with Dad that day or ever again. It was February 24th, their 58th wedding anniversary.

> 1 THESSALONIANS 2:4b NLT
>
> *Our purpose is to please God, not people. He is the One Who examines the motives of our hearts.*

Although Mom didn't have a full understanding of what was happening to their lives, she was suffering from the complete disruption of her world and the disorientation of being in a new place and without Dad. She wanted to get out of there and go home. Our mother, who exemplified social grace and had tried to teach us to be similarly disciplined and appropriate in our behavior, was unable to control either her situation or her response to it.

We had been advised, and we believe properly, to avoid visits for the first few days while the staff members helped Mom through this difficult time. For Dad, the period spent waiting for time and proper medication to help Mom become accustomed to her new environment was excruciating. Relying on second-hand reports about her progress was too hard for Dad, and he would slip over to the unit just to catch a glimpse of her. During Mom's first days on the unit, Dad even tried to spend some time with her, but his visits were always disruptive for Mom and only served to intensify his pain.

> PSALM 6:6–7b, 9 NIV
>
> *I am worn out from groaning;*
>   *all night long I flood my bed with weeping*
>   *and drench my couch with tears.*
> *My eyes grow weak with sorrow;*
> *... The LORD has heard my cry for mercy;*
>   *The LORD accepts my prayer.*

Eventually, the situation improved. Dad used to mark a plus or a minus on his calendar, depending on how Mom's day had gone. At first, there were only minuses, but soon, a few plusses started to appear, and finally, the days were mostly plusses. Mom had made the transition. The horror of Alzheimer's is that sufferers lose their memories, but this is also a blessing. Mom soon forgot her former life and settled into the simpler routine of daily living on the Alzheimer's wing.

In many ways, the change was tougher for Dad. He remembered everything. He tried to put up a brave front, but we often entered his home and found him red-eyed, just gazing out his window.

But God is merciful. Weeks passed, and we all felt blessed as we realized that Mom and Dad's journey together would continue. We hold a picture indelibly etched in our minds of

Mom running down the hall with her arms spread wide and a smile that only seeing Dad could bring to her face. We often found them sitting peacefully side by side, holding hands, not saying much but not needing to. Before he left, Dad would pull the little white bottle out of his pocket and turn to Mom: "Okay, Luv, here are my eye drops. Could you give me a hand?"

Your Guide

The day may come when you can no longer care for your loved one. The Alzheimer's sufferer may develop a tendency to wander away from home, the inability to handle appliances safely, sleeplessness, incontinence, loss of personal hygiene skills, and unchecked emotions. Any combination of these problems may make it impossible for you to continue to serve as the primary caregiver. The decision to move your loved one to a specialized Alzheimer's care facility will be one of the most difficult ones you ever have to make. Call on your support team to help you and keep focused on the knowledge that you're doing what's best.

> 1 PETER 4:19 NIV
>
> *So then, those who suffer according to God's will should commit themselves to their faithful Creator and continue to do good.*

Evaluating and Selecting an Alzheimer's Facility

If you are not already part of a community that offers a continuum of care, you will need to select a new residence that caters to the special needs of your loved one. Visit facilities you are considering on several occasions and at different times of the day. Consider the following factors as you evaluate the options and make a choice:

- Proximity to caregiver

- State licensing status

- Ombudsman reports regarding complaints

- Availability and quality of on-site medical services

Probably the most important factor contributing to excellence in care is an adequate level of staffing with qualified caregivers. We suggest seeking answers to the following questions before you make your decision:

- What is the training program for Alzheimer's care providers?

- What is the ratio of patients to staff who are actively involved with their care?

- What is the staff turnover rate?

In facilities we've visited, we've seen staff involvement with patients ranging from caring, hands-on interaction to detached neglect. Staff members should be assigned to the Alzheimer's unit long-term so that they develop relationships with patients, rather than being rotated through the Alzheimer's unit, assisted living, and skilled nursing. Again, ask yourself these questions as you consider available options:

- Do patients appear to be unusually sleepy and possibly overly medicated?

- Has the staff made an effort to keep the patients clean and neat?

- Are residents engaged in appropriate activities that they seem to enjoy?

- Does the staff interact with residents in a friendly manner, or are staff members occupied watching television, filling out paperwork, or socializing with one another?

- Does the staff know the whereabouts of all patients?

- Are most residents in a central location, or are many of them sitting in their own rooms or wandering inappropriately into areas where they do not belong?

- Does the staff intervene appropriately in dealing with patient anxiety or resistance?

- Are residents encouraged to feed themselves and stay as independent as possible for as long as possible?

- Is a security system in place that detects patients leaving the area?

> 2 TIMOTHY 1:14 NLT
>
> *With the help of the Holy Spirit Who lives within us, carefully guard what has been entrusted to you.*

As you research options and make visits, you will find that staff members who are actively involved in caregiving can give you helpful insight into the management and organization of their facilities. When you have the opportunity to speak privately, ask caregivers the questions outlined below to learn whether or not the facility lives up to its advertising:

Ask this question:	To find out:
What is your job description?	Is spending time with patients the primary focus of the staff?
If you see a procedure that should be changed, how do you address it?	Does management support staff decisions regarding their responsibilities?
How did you get this job assignment?	Do staff members want to be working in an Alzheimer's unit?
How do you feel at the end of a shift?	Do employees feel that the shifts they work are reasonable?
Who helps you?	Do employees have enough help when they're on duty?
How do you bond with your patients?	Do employees have primary responsibility for a few patients, or do they perform specific tasks for every patient?
For what housekeeping duties are you responsible?	Do housekeeping or laundry duties take staff away from patient care?
What's your favorite part of the job?	Do staff members truly enjoy caring for people?
Would you want your parents to live here?	What is the staff's general opinion of the facility?

The move to an Alzheimer's facility will bring many unavoidable changes to your loved one's life. Look for a place that feels as much like home as possible. Consider the following factors when making your decision:

- Cleanliness

- Absence of unpleasant odors

- Limited intrusion by loud intercoms, buzzers, and other institutional noises

- Pleasant and comfortable dining

- Appealing, nutritious food

- Morning and afternoon snacks

- Availability of fruit juices

- Soft, natural lighting

- Attractive, thoughtful decorating

- Resident-appropriate music and television or videos

- Comfortable seating for residents and visitors

- Opportunity to bring additional furniture and decorator items for patients' rooms

- Hair and nail care services

- In-room bathroom and shower

- Availability of religious services and pastoring

- Regular live entertainment, such as vocal or instrumental music concerts, sing-alongs, and performances by children's groups

- Presence of community pet(s)

- Secure patio, garden, or other outside area

Preparing for the Move

In an ideal situation, you would have time to make a number of preparations before moving your loved one. In reality, the move may happen quite suddenly, in which case necessary arrangements can be completed immediately thereafter.

Preparing clothing for the move is the biggest and most immediate task. All clothing, including socks and shoes, should be clearly labeled with a permanent marker. This is almost always a requirement. Clothing occasionally ends up in the wrong room after being laundered or when other residents unwittingly "borrow" things.

Institutional laundry services are extremely hard on clothing. Because Mom's clothes need to be replaced much more frequently now, we look for inexpensive and durable but comfortable items. In choosing clothing for your loved one, look for:

- Items that can be put on and taken off easily

- Loose-fitting slacks with elastic waists

- Garments that are washable; nothing that requires dry cleaning or cold-water washing

- Permanent-press fabrics

- Lots of underwear and socks

- Comfortable shoes and slippers

- Soft material, as sensory stimulation becomes more and more important

The Alzheimer's patient may take comfort in being surrounded by familiar furnishings. Chairs that the patient and primary caregiver used previously will make the new room feel more like home, although covering fabric seats with plastic may be prudent. If space permits, two chairs are better than one. Depending on what furniture is provided, you may want to bring in an additional dresser.

In-room televisions can needlessly expose patients to distressing programming and discourage socialization. Even seemingly appropriate TV programs may contain disturbing imagery. Soon after Mom moved to the Alzheimer's facility, she became upset and agitated by a plane crash she had seen on the TV in the common room. For this reason, we have chosen not to keep a TV in Mom's room, although most facilities allow them in patient rooms. Mom does have a CD player because listening to music is soothing to her. Her caregivers are thoughtful about turning it on when she is resting in her room.

> PSALM 84:3a NIV
>
> *Even the sparrow has found a home,*
> *and the swallow a nest for herself...*

Personalizing the room can be accomplished by hanging pictures of landscapes, flowers, animals, and children. Family photos become less meaningful to the patient but may be nice for caregivers and visitors. You may also select a bedspread or comforter and decorative pillows that are in keeping with the patient's taste and coordinate well with both the décor of the room and the other furniture you provide. As the behavior of Alzheimer's patients becomes more childlike, stuffed animals and dolls may be comforting to them, as well as adding to the warmth of the room.

We recommend that you do not take valuables of any kind to your loved one's new room, because security cannot be guaranteed. The patients' belongings are open to staff members, residents, and visitors. Rather than losing valuable jewelry, money, or irreplaceable family mementos, be creative in making substitutions. Things that are valuable and/or meaningful to the family are often no longer appreciated by the patient. We placed several valuable items in Mom's room that we thought she would like to have with her. When she showed no recollection, we removed them.

Accomplishing the Move

Moving the Alzheimer's patient into specialized care will probably be one of the most difficult jobs for the primary caregiver. Seek out others who have been through the process or have loved ones in the same residence. Lean on friends and family. Many people—both patients and family members—may need to see their physicians for additional prescription medication during this period.

> ROMANS 8:38–39 NIV
>
> *For I am convinced that neither death nor life, neither angels nor demons, neither the present nor the future, nor any powers, neither height nor depth, nor anything else in all creation, will be able to separate us from the love of God that is in Christ Jesus our Lord.*

Above all, allow yourself to feel good about all you've done for your loved one in caring for him or her thus far.

Staff members from the Alzheimer's unit should be helpful with all aspects of the transition. They will shoulder the burden, particularly during the early stages, when you can expect the patient to be confused, resistant, and distressed. In our experience, this behavior usually diminishes within two weeks or less. As difficult as this may be for you, patients may adjust more quickly if family visits are limited during the transition period. A quick phone call to the staff can give you the reassurance you need, while giving your loved one the necessary time to adapt to the new environment.

Supporting the Patient after the Move

We do not know of any Alzheimer's facilities that prohibit visits to your loved one at virtually any time. We encourage frequent, but not necessarily lengthy, visits after the initial period of adjustment. Stopping by at different times of the day and on different days of the week gives you a more accurate picture of the overall care being provided.

Let the staff know about favorite foods and music preferences. When new caregivers join the staff, take time to welcome them and acquaint them with your loved one's situation—how independent he or she is in eating, dressing, and personal hygiene. Inform new staff members of anything that makes your loved one particularly uncomfortable, such as bright lights, darkness, loud noises, even gentle squeezing of arthritic joints.

It's best to let the professional caregivers do what they're trained to do—feed, give showers, change clothes. Your time with your loved one can now be free of the stress and responsibility of day-to-day care. Staff members may not perform certain tasks in the same way or with the same level of care and attention that you would, but unless you have concerns about your loved one's health and safety, you should learn to keep a balanced perspective. We carefully arrange the clothes in our mother's closet in coordinated outfits, but the staff members don't always dress her in matching pants and blouses. Over time, we've come to accept the fact that if Mom's attire is occasionally unconventional or her hair is not styled once in a while, it really doesn't affect her quality of life. As long as she's clean and safe, her happiness is far more important than her appearance.

After the first month in her new home, we found that taking Mom out for brief periods of time was amazingly easy. She enjoyed attending chapel services, getting her hair done at the beauty parlor, going to the deli for lunch, or just sitting outside in the sunshine. Mom always had a good time but was happy and relieved to be "back home."

We know several families who, after a period of time, were able to take their loved ones to their homes for holidays or on brief outings. We recommend taking such actions in small steps and being sensitive to the comfort level of both the patient and yourself. As the disease progressed in our mother, she became somewhat frightened in situations involving a lot of activity; for this reason, we have chosen not to expose her to large family gatherings. Instead, we encourage everyone to visit her whenever the opportunity presents itself—for a brief period and not with more than a few people at a time.

Developing relationships with families of other residents can be a blessing. Only the family of an Alzheimer's patient can understand and relate to what you're experiencing. Look for opportunities to get to know the relatives of other residents in the facility. Not only will you start to look out for one another's loved ones, but you will each gain members for your support team.

As the primary advocate for your loved one, you still have an important role to play, but you have moved from a hands-on position to the responsibility of supervisor. Get to know the facility caregivers and their managers. When concerns arise, communicate them to the appropriate staff members immediately. If you aren't satisfied with the response, put your communication in writing, always retaining a copy for yourself. Your loved one can no longer effectively communicate needs and desires, and you have the ability and the responsibility to give voice to these unspoken appeals.

> PROVERBS 31:8–9 NASB
>
> *Open your mouth for the mute,*
> *For the rights of all the unfortunate.*
> *Open your mouth, judge righteously,*
> *And defend the rights of the afflicted*
> *and needy.*

Dad had us handle some of the communications with the facility management. He wanted to devote his energies to loving Mom, and he enjoyed their time together in her new place. Although our Dad didn't live in the Alzheimer's unit, he was comfortable there and became part of its family. He knew the residents, their families, and the caregivers. It became his second home.

A Prayer

Heavenly Father, You gave us Your Son, and He has assured us that we will never be separated from Your love. Thank You for always hearing and answering our prayers. Ease our pain and help us adjust to the new roles brought about by the physical separation from our loved one. Guide us to the comfort and hope that is found in Your Word. Thy will be done. In Jesus' name, Amen.

A Command and a Promise from God's Word

1 PETER 5:2, 4 NIV

Be shepherds of God's flock that is under your care, serving as overseers—not because you must, but because you are willing, as God wants you to be...And when the Chief Shepherd appears, you will receive the crown of glory that will never fade away.

Additional Scriptures

PSALM 22:24 NLT

> *For He has not ignored the suffering of the needy.*
>   *He has not turned and walked away.*
>   *He has listened to their cries for help.*

PSALM 94:17–19 NLT

> *Unless the LORD had helped me,*
>   *I would soon have died.*
> *I cried out, "I'm slipping!"*
>   *and Your unfailing love, O LORD, supported me.*
> *When doubts filled my mind,*
>   *Your comfort gave me renewed hope and cheer.*

PSALM 116:5–6 NIV

> *The LORD is gracious and righteous;*
>   *our God is full of compassion.*
> *The LORD protects the simplehearted;*
>   *when I was in great need, He saved me.*

PSALM 142:1–3a NLT

> *I cry out to the LORD;*
>   *I plead for the LORD's mercy.*
> *I pour out my complaints before Him*
>   *and tell Him all my troubles.*
> *For I am overwhelmed,*
>   *and You alone know the way I should turn.*

2 CORINTHIANS 1:3–4 NLT

All praise to the God and Father of our Lord Jesus Christ. He is the source of every mercy and the God Who comforts us. He comforts us in all our troubles so that we can comfort others. When others are troubled, we will be able to give them the same comfort God has given us.

2 CORINTHIANS 4:6 NLT

For God, Who said, "Let there be light in the darkness," has made us understand that this light is the brightness of the glory of God that is seen in the face of Jesus Christ.

1 TIMOTHY 1:12 NIV

I thank Christ Jesus Our Lord, Who has given me strength, that He considered me faithful, appointing me to His service.

Chapter 10: A New Beginning

What is His plan for me now?

Our Story

*" Hi, is this the front desk? This is one of the Nimz girls.
Do you happen to know where our father is?"*

Keeping tabs on Dad had become increasingly difficult
since he'd moved from the patio home into an apartment over-
looking Mom's room in the Alzheimer's wing. His new home
in the main building seemed to have been handpicked by God.
It was the only one available when he was ready to move, and
it was a special gift that Dad felt he could still "keep an eye" on
Mom.

That evening, Dad was again found sitting in the comfortable lobby across from the front desk. He had become a "lob-
byist," a regular in the group that routinely gathered there to
visit following dinner. Dad would take a seat and join in the
friendly conversation after performing his nightly ritual, leaving
a mint for the receptionist at the front desk.

As he took his place this evening, one of his fitness-center buddies said, "Al, I hear they're going to add an extra day to the exercise class schedule in January. Are you going to sign up?"

"Absolutely. I wouldn't miss it. I'm not breaking any speed records, but I think I've finally got the hang of that elliptical machine."

Dad turned to one of the ladies in the group: "By the way, I've got a pretty good stack of mail piling up. If I bring some along tomorrow evening, can I get you to read it to me?"

"Oh, Al, my granddaughter has been here, and we've been having such a good time that I forgot to check to see if you needed any help. She left this afternoon, and I'll be happy to take care of your mail. Bring it with you tomorrow, and we'll get you caught up."

Dad had learned that accepting help from others in the retirement community was good for both parties. He needed assistance with reading his mail, and others needed more of a sense of purpose. They took turns giving and receiving help. The evening conversations of the lobbyists provided the perfect opportunity for them to share in one another's burdens and joys. Dad's support group had grown significantly since he and Mom had moved to the retirement community.

> PHILIPPIANS 2:4 NIV
>
> *Each of you should look not only to your own interests, but also to the interests of others.*

Many evenings, Dad would excuse himself for a few minutes to ride the circuit with the driver as the community van delivered friends from his "old neighborhood" back to their homes. The ride also gave Dad a chance to catch up on events in the life of the driver, one of the many friends he'd made among the staff at the retirement community.

Dad especially enjoyed riding with a former neighbor whose wife was in the Alzheimer's unit with Mom. He and his friend often ate dinner together and checked on each other's wives when they visited their own. Even after Dad moved to his apartment, the two gentlemen continued their practice of calling each other every morning. It was a reassuring way to start the day for both of them. They counted on each other.

On those rare occasions when we would find Dad in his apartment, he would be listening to his favorite hymns and reading his Bible or one of the many devotional books that were always spread out on the couch. He needed large print now and the help of a lighted magnifying glass. Although reading had become difficult for him, spending time in prayer and reading the Bible remained his first priorities.

In Dad's pocket was the small spiral notebook that he always carried with him. It was his prayer list. As people and their needs came to mind, Dad would jot down a reminder to include them in his prayers. He was a prayer warrior and his list was long.

> JAMES 5:16b NIV
>
> *The prayer of a righteous man is powerful and effective.*

He prayed for family, for old friends and new, for the United States, its leaders and military, for the church, for the poor, for the sick, for those who were grieving, for peace, for large things and small. He prayed for the staff in the community that had become his home—for the caregivers in the Alzheimer's unit who were entrusted with his wife's well-being, for the ladies in the deli who faithfully prepared his favorite lunches and saved him a coconut macaroon, for the housekeepers who were careful not to disrupt the apartment of a visually impaired resident, for the van drivers who were so kind to Mom when they had first moved to the community, for the maintenance man who was teaching him Spanish, and for the security guard who checked on Dad when he saw his light on late at night.

He always included the prayer "For the Aged," from *The Book of Common Prayer of the Episcopal Church:*

> *Look with mercy, O God our Father, on all whose increasing years bring them weakness, distress, or isolation. Provide for them homes of dignity and peace; give them understanding helpers, and the willingness to accept help; and, as their strength diminishes, increase their faith, and their assurance of Your love. This we ask in the name of Jesus Christ our Lord. Amen*

Every time he prayed throughout the day, he closed with the prayer that never fails:

Lord, Thy will be done.

It had been almost a year since Mom had moved into the Alzheimer's unit, but Dad still hesitated to be away from her. When Ann invited him to spend a few days at her home in Texas, the decision to go was difficult for him. But Ann had timed the invitation to coincide with a visit from her daughter and family, and Dad was excited about the opportunity to see them and meet his newest great granddaughter for the first time. He hadn't forgotten the pastor's words the day he and Mom left Wisconsin: *"...There's a mission for you...to reach out to your grandchildren and for them to get to know you...grandparents have a unique role to play in the lives of their grandchildren."* When he was doing his slow laps in Ann's pool, playing with balloons with his great granddaughters, helping Ann with a school project, and leading the family in meal-time prayer, he knew his decision to visit Texas was the right one.

> ACTS 20:24 NLT
>
> *But my life is worth nothing unless I use it for doing the work assigned me by the Lord Jesus—the work of telling others the Good News about God's wonderful kindness and love.*

Upon his return from a wonderful week in Texas, Dad had a pretty good pile of Mom's laundry waiting for him. We were amused by the fact that he enjoyed doing this loving service for her, particularly because he had never done laundry before in his life. He was proud of his newly acquired skill and delighted in giving us tips for doing our own wash. He had developed the habit of moving outside of his comfort zone, of trying new things.

From the time Mom had moved to the Alzheimer's floor, Dad had been a regular in the unit. He knew all the residents by name, as well as many of their family members. He had a way of connecting with everyone on an individual and personal basis. The staff enjoyed Dad and got to know him well. It was a source of sadness to him that they had never had a chance to know Mom in the same way.

From time to time, the staff would catch glimpses into Mom's and Dad's unique personalities and the love they had for each other. Their devotion could be seen as they sat and held hands in the deepening shadows of a Virginia afternoon. Or as Mom ran with outstretched arms to meet Dad as he came down the hall toward her room. And finally, although they didn't know it at the time, as they danced their last dance in the soft light of the Christmas party— Dad in his bright red sports jacket, holding Mom in her periwinkle blue dress.

> ### 1 CORINTHIANS 13:4a, 7–8a NLT
>
> *Love is patient and kind....Love never gives up, never loses faith, is always hopeful, and endures through every circumstance. Love will last forever...*

Your Guide

Giving up your duties as primary caregiver brings significant changes to your life. The days that were formerly filled to overflowing with the innumerable tasks involved in caring for your loved one may now loom before you—seemingly void of purpose and painfully lonely.

Whatever your situation, we recommend that you start your

recovery with prayer and time spent with the Lord and the Bible. In some cases, getting your life back on track will be fairly easy. In other cases, it may require tremendous strength of will. For some people, professional help and medication may be needed. If you are experiencing more than a couple of the following symptoms, you may be suffering from debilitating depression and should seek help from a physician or counselor:

- Lack of energy or interest in daily activities

- Apathy, inability to get up and moving in the morning

- Waves of sadness and emptiness

- The desire to be alone

- Feelings of worthlessness or hopelessness

- Indifference to your appearance

- Changes in eating or sleeping habits

- Irritability

- Thoughts of suicide

> ZECHARIAH 4:6b NIV
>
> *"'Not by might nor by power, but by My Spirit,' says the LORD Almighty."*

Trying to regain your physical strength is an important first step in recovering from the demands of being the primary caregiver to a person with advancing Alzheimer's. Physical activity will not only help your body recover, but it also will improve your emotional well-being. You should, however, check with your physician before starting any exercise program.

Try different forms of exercise, then continue with the ones you like doing. "The best form of exercise is anything you'll do." After getting your doctor's approval, try one or more of these activities or others that you enjoy:

- Walking with a partner

- Swimming or doing water aerobics

- Dancing

- Taking an exercise class

- Joining a gym or fitness center

- Working out with a personal trainer

- Gardening

Physical recovery is vital, but it is only part of the process. Equally or more important is the need to be socially active. Spending time with friends and family doesn't just pass time; it also helps to fill the empty space that has been left by your separation from your loved one. Some people are ready for social interaction sooner than others, but as soon as you are able to, seek out opportunities to socialize. Try some of the following suggestions:

> 1 JOHN 1:7a NLT
>
> *But if we are living in the light of God's presence, just as Christ is, then we have fellowship with each other...*

- Accept all invitations and invite people to your home or to accompany you on an outing.

- Join a book club or Bible study group.

- Participate in a bridge or Mah Jong group or a poker club.

- Attend sporting events and concerts with friends.

- Get a pet.

- Visit relatives.

- Participate in church activities.

- Join an Alzheimer's support group—many are sponsored by the Alzheimer's Association.

- Volunteer through your church, senior center, community center, or local schools.

Learning something new is stimulating, motivating, and rewarding. While you've been a full-time caregiver, you haven't had time to pursue your own interests. Now you have time to take advantage of new opportunities; examples include the following:

- Take a class—in a foreign language, computer science, sewing, or music appreciation.

- Travel—visit relatives, take a cruise, go on a group tour to a far-off place, or sign up for some day trips.

- Develop your artistic side—play an instrument, become an author, join a theatre group, or learn sculpting, painting, ceramics, woodworking, flower arranging, or photography.

- Make regular trips to libraries and museums.

As you are healing, reach out to help others. You have gained invaluable knowledge and experience in your journey with

Alzheimer's. Sharing helps you heal as you see the burden of others lightened through your willingness to listen and respond with loving kindness. As you focus your attention on the needs of others, you may find that your own troubles lose their intensity and no longer have the power to overwhelm you. You're probably already familiar with many ways you can be of assistance to others:

- Be a good listener.

- Pray for and with others.

- Relieve primary caregivers by sitting with their loved ones.

- Share information gained through your experience.

- Visit or phone someone who is isolated.

- Take a caregiver and/or the patient out for a drive, to a meal, to church, or to some other activity.

- Run errands for a primary caregiver.

- Volunteer at a hospital, a school, your church, a library, or a charitable organization.

- Send cards and write letters.

- Cook for a shut-in.

- Read to the blind.

> 1 PETER 4:10 NIV
>
> *Each one should use whatever gift he has received to serve others, faithfully administering God's grace in its various forms.*

Our Dad was an inspirational role model for this transition. We were particularly touched to learn he was sitting with a neighbor who had Alzheimer's so that the man's wife could get a much needed break from her caregiving duties. Dad was grieving deeply, weakened by years of caregiving, and had severe vision and hearing impairments. Nonetheless, through the grace of God and Dad's unwavering faith, he persevered in his lifestyle of reaching out in love to each and every person in his path.

A Prayer

Heavenly Father, we praise Your tenderness, mercy, and love. It is You Who gives us hope in our suffering, joy in our sorrow. Lead us down the path of everlasting love, doing the work assigned to us by Jesus and using our gifts to serve others. Grant us Your peace as we come to the end of our struggles. Thy will be done. In Jesus' name, Amen.

Assurance from God's Word

JAMES 5:10–11 NLT

For examples of patience in suffering, dear brothers and sisters, look at the prophets who spoke in the name of the Lord. We give great honor to those who endure under suffering. Job is an example of a man who endured patiently. From his experience we see how the Lord's plan finally ended in good, for He is full of tenderness and mercy.

Additional Scriptures

PSALM 25:4–5 NLT

> *Show me the path where I should walk, O LORD;*
> *point out the right road for me to follow.*
> *Lead me by Your truth and teach me,*
> *for You are the God Who saves me.*
> *All day long I put my hope in You.*

PSALM 40:1–3 NLT

> *I waited patiently for the LORD to help me,*
> *and He turned to me and heard my cry.*
> *He lifted me out of the pit of despair,*
> *out of the mud and the mire.*
> *He set my feet on solid ground*
> *and steadied me as I walked along.*
> *He has given me a new song to sing,*
> *a hymn of praise to our God.*
> *Many will see what He has done and be astounded.*
> *They will put their trust in the LORD.*

PSALM 91:1–2 NLT

> *Those who live in the shelter of the Most High*
> *will find rest in the shadow of the Almighty.*
> *This I declare of the LORD:*
> *He alone is my refuge, my place of safety;*
> *He is my God, and I am trusting Him.*

ROMANS 15:13 NIV

> *May the God of hope fill you with all joy and peace as you*
> *trust in Him, so that you may overflow with hope by the*
> *power of the Holy Spirit.*

PHILIPPIANS 3:12b–14 NLT

...I keep working toward that day when I will finally be all that Christ Jesus saved me for and wants me to be. No, dear brothers and sisters, I am still not all I should be, but I am focusing all my energies on this one thing: Forgetting the past and looking forward to what lies ahead, I strain to reach the end of the race and receive the prize for which God, through Christ Jesus, is calling us up to heaven.

1 PETER 1:6–7 NLT

So be truly glad! There is wonderful joy ahead, even though it is necessary for you to endure many trials for a while.

These trials are only to test your faith, to show that it is strong and pure. It is being tested as fire tests and purifies gold—and your faith is far more precious to God than mere gold. So if your faith remains strong after being tried by fiery trials, it will bring you much praise and glory and honor on the day when Jesus Christ is revealed to the whole world.

1 PETER 3:15 NIV

But in your hearts set apart Christ as Lord. Always be prepared to give an answer to everyone who asks you to give the reason for the hope that you have. But do this with gentleness and respect...

Epilogue

Dad told us about the Christmas party in great detail the next day from a bed in the emergency room. We had been called there in the early hours of Christmas Eve morning. It was not the first time we had been to the hospital with Dad. His health was failing, and the medical staff at the retirement community was always cautious. We were concerned but not alarmed.

We later learned that Dad had been living with a lot of pain, something he had hidden from us. We found out that when he was having a bad day, the maintenance man would go down to check on Mom for him. Although he had planned to attend a family gathering at the home of one of his grandsons that evening, test results had come back, and instead, he was heading for emergency surgery. Our concern was growing, and we called distant family members to gather at the hospital.

Because of the holiday, much of the family was already in the area. We had some quiet moments with Dad while we were waiting for the surgeon to arrive. It seemed important to him that we be able to picture our Mom and Dad dancing together at the Christmas party the night before. He talked about how beautiful Mom was and noted with pleasure that she was wearing his favorite periwinkle blue dress. He asked about our families and seemed to savor every detail that we shared.

We talked for a long time, but our conversation came to a close when we were informed that the surgeon had arrived. As we gathered closer to Dad's bed, he held each of our hands, looked with compassion into our teary eyes, and said, "Love and peace to all."

We walked beside him as he was wheeled down the hall and into the room adjoining the operating room. He kept repeating, "Love and peace to all." It was his final message to us.

> REVELATION 21:4–5a KJV
>
> *And God shall wipe away all tears from their eyes; and there shall be no more death, neither sorrow, nor crying, neither shall there be any more pain: for the former things are passed away. And He that sat upon the throne said, Behold, I make all things new.*

The next day, more family members joined us. The news was not hopeful. Richard, Nancy's husband, left the hospital to be with Mom. Late that afternoon, surrounded by his family and lifted up on the wings of prayer, Dad left us to be with his precious Lord and Savior. It was Christmas Day.

We spent the next several days in Dad's apartment planning his memorial service. We took comfort in being in his home. One day at lunchtime we headed down to the deli, one of

Dad's favorite stops. His friends behind the counter recognized us and were particularly thoughtful, knowing that we were grieving. When we finished ordering, we followed Dad's custom of handing over his wallet to the cashier and saying, "Just take what you need." An excruciating sob filled the room. We were stunned by her reaction and told her how sorry we were—we hadn't meant to cause her pain. She couldn't speak for a minute but shook her head and walked away from us. She clearly needed a moment to compose herself.

"Why did you have to do that?" she asked when she returned.

"We wanted you to know how much it means to us that our Dad could trust you in his failing sight."

As we hugged, she said, "I loved your Dad."

"We know you did. He loved you, too."

We experienced many moments like this one as we encountered Dad's friends and neighbors over the next few days. Residents and staff alike had been influenced by Dad's daily walk in Christian love.

In addition to his loving spirit, he carried a tall, weathered walking stick with him everywhere he went, a gift from Peggy's husband, Hal. You could find it outside the dining room when he was having dinner. It accompanied him to the Alzheimer's unit and on visits to our homes. On Sunday mornings, it was propped against the wall outside the chapel. It was always with him.

Packing up Dad's belongings took only a few days. He had

been walking toward his eternal home for a long time. We loaded the last boxes on the cart, turned off the lights, and closed the door. Dad's walking stick was still propped up in the hallway. To us, it was a visual reminder of his steadfast journey through the last years of his life. To his neighbors, the walking stick had been a sign that he was home.

> ISAIAH 26:12 NIV
>
> *LORD, You establish peace for us;*
> *all that we have accomplished You have done for us.*

One of the few blessings of our mother's experience with Alzheimer's was that it protected her from the unbearable pain of losing the great love of her life. In keeping with Dad's final message of "Love and peace to all," we prayed long and hard about how to tell Mom of his death. We knew she was incapable of understanding and unable to retain the thought. We simply told her that Dad was with Jesus, and she was happy with that.

The retirement community had provided the perfect environment for Dad, but in our experience, the optimum community for the caregiver does not always include an optimum facility for the Alzheimer's patient. Within a month of Dad's death, we moved Mom to a place much closer to family, where we could spend more time with her and more actively oversee her care. The difference this move made in her day-to-day existence was dramatic. With a larger, well-trained staff and an environment specifically geared to the special needs of the Alzheimer's patient, she settled in quickly.

Although we were happy with the care she received at the second facility, when circumstances changed, we decided to move her again. This new facility was even closer to us, was owned by the same organization, and had recently opened an Alzheimer's unit. We were pleased that Mom never realized she was in a new place and, therefore, never suffered through a difficult period of adjustment.

Shortly after Mom's move, Nancy's mother-in-law, Grace, moved into an assisted-living wing two floors above Mom. The sight of the two gray heads close together, just being comfortable with each other, was touching. The two women had been friends for more than 40 years, and both enjoyed the visits until Grace left to be with the Lord in 2004.

Mom is still there as we write this book and is nearing 90. She was diagnosed with Alzheimer's disease 13 years ago. Physically, she is doing remarkably well. Although Alzheimer's has won the battle for Mom's mind, the Holy Spirit is alive and

> ## 1 Peter 3:3–4 NASB
>
> *Your adornment must not be merely external—braiding the hair, and wearing gold jewelry, or putting on dresses; but let it be the hidden person of the heart, with the imperishable quality of a gentle and quiet spirit, which is precious in the sight of God.*

well in her soul. She has been robbed of her memories, but they have been replaced with a peaceful, almost childlike quality. When we look into her eyes now, we see the love and peace that was Dad's prayer for her.

A Benediction

May our Heavenly Father bless your family as you journey through Alzheimer's disease. May He guide you and bring you closer to one another and closer to Him. And finally, may He grant you His love and His peace. Thy will be done. In Jesus' name, Amen.

A Promise from God's Word

1 PETER 5:10 NIV

And the God of all grace, Who called you to His eternal glory in Christ, after you have suffered a little while, will Himself restore you and make you strong, firm and steadfast.

Additional Scriptures

PSALM 16:11 NLT

You will show me the way of life,
granting me the joy of Your presence
and the pleasures of living with You forever.

PSALM 17:15 NLT

But because I have done what is right, I will see You.
When I awake, I will be fully satisfied,
for I will see You face to face.

PSALM 73:23–24 NIV

Yet I am always with You;
You hold me by my right hand.
You guide me with Your counsel,
and afterward You will take me into glory.

JOHN 14:1–3 KJV

Let not your heart be troubled: ye believe in God, believe also in Me. In My Father's house are many mansions: if it were not so, I would have told you. I go to prepare a place for you. And if I go and prepare a place for you, I will come again, and receive you unto Myself; that where I am, there ye may be also.

2 CORINTHIANS 3:17, 18b NLT

Now, the Lord is the Spirit, and wherever the Spirit of the Lord is, He gives freedom. And as the Spirit of the Lord works within us, we become more and more like Him and reflect His glory even more.

2 CORINTHIANS 4:17 NIV

For our light and momentary troubles are achieving for us an eternal glory that far outweighs them all.

2 CORINTHIANS 5:1–2, 8 NLT

For we know that when this earthly tent we live in is taken down—when we die and leave these bodies—we will have a home in heaven, an eternal body made for us by God Himself and not by human hands. We grow weary in our present bodies, and we long for the day when we will put on our heavenly bodies like new clothing.

Yes, we are fully confident, and we would rather be away from these bodies, for then we will be at home with the Lord.

For the Reader from God's Word

COLOSSIANS 1:9–12 NLT

So we have continued praying for you ever since we first heard about you. We ask God to give you a complete understanding of what He wants to do in your lives, and we ask Him to make you wise with spiritual wisdom. Then the way you live will always honor and please the Lord, and you will continually do good, kind things for others. All the while, you will learn to know God better and better.

We also pray that you will be strengthened with His glorious power so that you will have all the patience and endurance you need. May you be filled with joy, always thanking the Father, Who has enabled you to share in the inheritance that belongs to God's holy people, who live in the light.

Additional Resources

Alzheimer's Association
www.alz.org
1-800-272-3900

Eldercare Locator
www.eldercare.gov
1-800-677-1116

Meals on Wheels Association of America
www.mowaa.org
1-703-548-5558

Bible Study Fellowship International
www.bsfinternational.org
1-877-273-3228

Recommended Reading

Today's Parallel Bible (Zondervan, 2000).

Why?: Trusting God When You Don't Understand,
Anne Graham Lotz (W Publishing Group, A Division of
Thomas Nelson Publishers, 2004).

31 Days of Praise, Ruth and Warren Myers
(Multnomah Publishers, Inc., 1994).

God's Words of Life (Zondervan Gift Products, 1997).

The Quiet Moments with God Series
(Honor Books, Inc., 1996).

Web Sites from Our Story

www.waupacaareachamber.com

www.riponmainst.com/riponmainst/hist.html

www.visitwaupaca.com/RED_MILL_GROUNDS.html

Acknowledgments

PSALM 115:1 NLT

Not to us, O LORD, but to You goes all the glory
for Your unfailing love and faithfulness.

We begin our earthly acknowledgments with our family. Each of you has played an important role in the lives of our parents and in the life of this book. You believed in us before we realized that God could do this through us.

Our husbands, Richard, Bill, and Hal, have been the sons our parents never had. We thank you for your time, your energy, your patience, and your love. Your unwavering, enthusiastic support has been a constant source of encouragement and has energized us to persevere as we struggled with the reliving of this often painful period of our lives.

Our amazing children and their spouses, Christie, Ted and Julie, Julie and Matt, Steve and Melissa, Kim and Tony, Ryan, Sara Anne, Debbie and Brian, Karin, Eric and Ida, have been a blessing in so many ways—all with their unique and loving contributions. You may never know how much you contributed to the lives of your grandparents. The joy of grandchildren cannot be overstated. God has also blessed us with grandchildren of our own: Steven, Daniel, Cassandra, Stephanie, Alex, Allyson, Kelly, Marissa, Madison, Lauren, Matthew, Kristina, Alyson, Bronwyn, and Linnea. As Bapa Nimz always said, "There's not a bad apple in the bunch."

Our husbands and children were eager and enthusiastic reviewers of the draft of *"Your Mother Has Alzheimer's."* We value your input, and your suggestions have added immeasurably to the quality and helpfulness of the book.

Chuck Nason was a continual source of encouragement, knowledge, and even refuge as we began and ended the first draft on the porch of his cottage. Chuck, it was your mother who coined the family expression, "Be a relative." We're so glad you listened to your mother.

Working with Debby Nolan, our smart, skilled, and speedy editor, has been a hoot. Her e-mails were almost always a source of humor and encouragement, and they arrived just when we needed a lift. On a number of occasions, when we couldn't seem to get the words right, one of us would say, "Debby will fix it." She always did. Thanks, Debby. You were the perfect person, at the perfect time, with the perfect skills!

Jackie Bray took the hodgepodge of old photos, sketches on scrap paper, and vague ideas we gave her and created the cover illustration and beautiful drawings that are scattered throughout the book. She was a stranger to us when we asked her to help with the project, but she has become our treasured sister in Christ. Jackie is a gifted illustrator, and we are blessed that she applied her incredible flexibility and vision to our book through her poignant artwork.

Clare Hendrix was also unknown to us when we approached Winchester Printers, Inc., about providing desktop publishing for our book. We quickly came to appreciate her outstanding design skills, excellent judgment, and dedication to our project. Clare, you took our manuscript and made it look like a real book.

Our heartfelt thanks to the people of Ripon, Wisconsin, who were supportive of our parents: Dave Duehring and the staff at Ripon Drug, the members of St. Peter's Episcopal Church, Father Ken and Grace Okkerse, Lee Nichols Otis, and Joyce and Don Lueck. Certainly there were additional friends and neighbors who were very helpful to our parents. Although we are unable to mention each of you by name, we want you to know that we appreciate everything that was done for Mom and Dad. We particularly thank our dear friend Sharon Evensen and her late husband Bob. They were faithful friends to our parents and to us. We all miss Bob's great smile and giving spirit.

Our parents had their earthly "Angel" to visit them, communicate their medical needs, and help us search out long-term care options. Her experience and love were always willingly available to Mom and Dad and to us whenever we called on her.

Once our parents relocated to Virginia, many excellent staff members, caring neighbors, and dear friends made their adjustment to the retirement community much easier than it might have been. Thank you all.

William Hienz, of Robert W. Baird & Company, went above and beyond his job description to make the move to Virginia possible. Bill continues to be an excellent steward of our parents' finances, and we are enormously grateful to him for his caring professionalism.

We are thankful to Cindy Gibbs, CPA, who began helping our father when his failing sight prevented him from keeping his own books. He considered Cindy his personal assistant, and she continues to take care of Mom's tax returns.

Nancy Gray, of Irvine Travel, scheduled and rescheduled our travel and accommodations with the patience of Job. She successfully coordinated arrivals and departures to and from four different parts of the country. Thanks, Nancy. You made it seem so easy, and we know it wasn't!

We are extremely appreciative of those who agreed to read our draft and comment: our immediate family members; Pastors Mark Carey and Don Den Hartog; Kathy Davies; Judy Davis; Sam and Faith Ensogna; Bob and Sharon Evensen; Chick Garnett; Sheri Harber and her mother; Elizabeth Mulloy; Chuck Nason; Father Ken and Grace Okkerse; Lee Nichols Otis; Eleanor Pridgen; Susan, Gordon, and Hans Schultz; Kay Seivert; and Robin Swoboda Wagner.

From start to finish, our cousin Chuck has been an important contributor to the success of this book. In July of 2004, we sat around the cottage table and shared our vision with

Chuck, his sister, Susan, and her husband, Gordon. We swapped stories about our parents' journeys through Alzheimer's, and the dream began to become reality. A year and a half later, Worzalla Publishing Company president and CEO Charles W. Nason (Cousin Chuck) was there to welcome us and share in the excitement as the first copies of *"Your Mother Has Alzheimer's"* rolled off the press. We are grateful for his support and that of our Worzalla customer service representative, Amy Ewald.

We are thankful for the wonderful caregivers who have lovingly and skillfully cared for our mother throughout the final stages of Alzheimer's disease. Both Sunrise at Hunter Mill and Sunrise at Reston Town Center have provided a warm and safe home for Mom.

We'll be forever grateful to our Florida support group: Billy Steeghs, our on-call computer wizard; Eleanor Pridgen, who makes it possible for Nancy to devote so much time to the book; and all those at Medical Development International who have wholeheartedly supported this project.

Beth Ricles, the principal at Lynn Hale Academy, Arlington, Texas, has been unwavering in her support and encouragement of Ann's becoming an author. Thank you, Beth, from all three of us.

Thanks also to Pam Wingfield, Rose Reisig, and Barry Cui, who have frequently taken on extra work so that Peggy could be away from Editech Services. Their interest in the book and their encouragement have been enthusiastic, and we are grateful for their support.

Special thanks to "our people." You know who you are, and so do we!

Our faith is at the center of our story, and we want to acknowledge Bible Study Fellowship and the teaching leaders and discussion leaders who have enriched our walk with God over the years. We are all active members, as are two of our daughters.

Although our names are on the cover, we believe that we had the perfect "Ghost Writer." As you can imagine, much of the narrative was painful and difficult to write. Prayer was our constant companion, and the Holy Spirit provided the words when we were unable to continue. He is a faithful and loving God.

PSALM 23 KJV

The LORD is my Shepherd; I shall not want.
He maketh me to lie down in green pastures:
He leadeth me beside the still waters.
He restoreth my soul:
He leadeth me in the paths of righteousness for His name's sake.
Yea, though I walk through the valley of the shadow of death,
I will fear no evil: for Thou art with me;
Thy rod and Thy staff they comfort me.
Thou preparest a table before me in the presence of mine enemies:
Thou anointest my head with oil; my cup runneth over.
Surely goodness and mercy shall follow me all the days of my life:
And I will dwell in the house of the LORD for ever.

Prayer Requests

_____

_____

_____

_____

_____

_____

_____

_____

_____

_____

_____

_____

_____

_____

Answers to Prayer

_____

_____

_____

_____

_____

_____

_____

_____

_____

_____

_____

_____

_____

How to Order

"Your Mother Has Alzheimer's"
Three daughters answer their father's call.
Margaret Byers • Ann Guyer • Nancy Willich

Web orders: www.yourmotherhasalzheimers.com

By telephone: 877-577-8885 (toll free)

By U.S. mail: ACord Publications, LLC
P.O. Box 979
Ponte Vedra Beach, FL 32004

I would like to order the following items:

	Quantity	Amount
"Your Mother Has Alzheimer's" – Book @ $15.95 each	_____	$_____
"Your Mother Has Alzheimer's" – CD @ $29.95 each	_____	$_____
Sales Tax: Add 6% for items shipped to Florida		$_____

For U.S. shipping, one book or CD – Add $4.00.
   For **each** additional book or CD – Add $2.00.
For overnight delivery – Call toll-free number.   Shipping: $_____

                                                                    Total: $_____

Name: _____

Address: _____

City: _____ State: _____ Zip: _____

Telephone: _____

Email: _____

Payment: ❑ Check Enclosed   ❑ MasterCard   ❑ Visa

Card Number: _____

Name on Card: _____

Expiration Date: _____

Signature: _____